BRIDGE ACROSS
THE ATLANTIC

BY THE SAME AUTHOR

NOVELS
Follow a Shadow (Cassell)
Port of Call (Cassell)
The Street that Died (Cassell)
Three Women (Cassell)
Good and Evil (Cassell)
Getting the Boy (Elek)

WAR
Rehearsal for Invasion (Harrap)
Some of it was Fun (Nelson)

SPORT
The World of Rugby (Elek)
The Lions (Paul)
The Unsmiling Giants (Paul)
Best Rugby Stories (ed.) (Faber)
The Rugby Companion (Paul)
There was also some Rugby (Paul)
A History of Rugby (Barker)

BIOGRAPHY
Frost: Anatomy of a Success (MacDonald)
Flushed with Pride: The Story of Thomas Crapper (MacDonald)
Bust Up: The Story of Otto Titzling (MacDonald)

The Inferior Sex (Prentice-Hall)

Bridge Across the Atlantic

THE STORY OF JOHN RENNIE

Wallace Reyburn

HARRAP   LONDON

To Major Rennie Maudslay

First Published in Great Britain 1972
by GEORGE G. HARRAP & CO. LTD
182–184 High Holborn, London WC1V 7AX

© *Wallace Reyburn* 1972

ISBN: 0 245 50888 0

*Composed in Linotype Caledonia and printed
by Western Printing Services Ltd, Bristol*

Made in Great Britain

Contents

Illustrations

1 *A Rival to Disneyland*

IT is appropriate that John Rennie's life span—1761–1821—fitted neatly into the period which came to be known as the Industrial Revolution. A farm boy who became one of the greatest engineers of the time, he epitomized that era from 1760 to 1840 which saw Britain transformed from a mainly agricultural country to one predominantly industrial.

His name is not as readily known as those which spring to mind when one thinks of the epoch when the engineers became the dominant force in the land: Hargreaves, with his spinning-jenny, and Arkwright, with the water-frame, who started it all by revolutionizing the textile trade; Brindley at the forefront of the men who gave Britain its network of canals; Macadam, forever identified with road construction; Telford, the bridge builder; Watt, of the steam engine; Stevenson, pioneer of railway transport: such men as these were his contemporaries. He ranked as high as any of them, higher than most, since his talents were spread over a much wider field than the majority of them. In his mature years so highly regarded was he that there were few projects of national importance on which he was not consulted. He was a versatile genius. But also he was a publicity-shunning Scot.

In 1817 at the opening of his Waterloo Bridge, considered one of the most magnificent stone bridges ever built, the Prince Regent (later George IV) wanted to confer a knighthood upon him on the spot. Rennie asked leave to refuse it and later wrote to a friend: 'I had a hard business to escape a knighthood at the opening.'

In London there were his two other great bridges—Southwark and London Bridge—and he was the man called in to solve the nineteenth-century problems of the world's largest port with the London and East India Docks. Today one cannot travel far in the United Kingdom without encountering something that was of his design or construction, whether it be a bridge, canal, viaduct, lighthouse, harbour . . . Kelso Bridge, Newhaven Harbour, the fifty-seven-miles-long Kennet and Avon Canal, Plymouth Breakwater, Hull Docks, the amazing Bell Rock Lighthouse, which appears to rise straight up out of the North Sea, Newton Stewart Bridge, the Datchet to Windsor Road, Dublin Docks and Belfast Harbour, the Lune Aqueduct outside Lancaster (referred to as 'possibly the finest bridge in the country'), Grimsby Docks, the Don Bridge in Aberdeen, the Dundas Aqueduct at Bath, Ramsgate Harbour. . . . It was said of Rennie:

> He bequeathed to posterity a series of structures the beauty of which is outstanding. His bridges and viaducts, his tunnels and aqueducts, were his contribution to fine architecture, and they bear the marks of a master. For handsome proportions, grace and beauty of line and delicacy of detail, they stand in a class apart; they have never been excelled and rarely equalled.

The reason he has not received from the general public full recognition for the great range of his achievements lies mainly in the very self-effacement that made it for him 'a hard business to avoid a knighthood'. Brought up in the dour Scottish background of East Linton, a then isolated community twenty-odd miles out towards the east coast from Edinburgh, he was displaying his genius as a mechanical engineer so early in life that on leaving school at sixteen he was brought back immediately to fill the post of master of mathematics. But from the time he set up in business for himself as a civil engineer at the age of eighteen he did not, like others in his field, hasten to the Patent Office to ensure that future generations would be made aware that it was he who had first evolved this or that new process, revolutionary method of construction or ingenious mechanical contrivance.

He was building 'macadamized' roads years before John Macadam was credited with the invention of the process. His ideas for developing the steam engine were so far-seeing that James Watt tried to get him to sign a paper promising that he would not turn his attention to that sphere of endeavour. He merely shrugged his shoulders when told that Sir Samuel Bentham had patented in his own name Rennie's revolutionary system for the construction of retaining walls for docks.

Rennie, the unacknowledged inventor, looked upon his innovations merely as part of the routine of his work. They came in the course of a working day, which started with his rising at 5 a.m.

and did not cease until midnight, and were for him just ways of saving labour or materials, ingeniously overcoming a specific problem or making for a more efficient product. Such improvements in technique he would carry over into future projects. If others copied him or sought to gain credit for ideas that were his, it was something about which he did not concern himself.

Overseas the works of John Rennie are to be seen at such widely scattered points as Bombay, Naples, Cape Town, Lucknow, Malta and Leningrad. And now in the United States one may see one of his most important contributions to civil engineering—London Bridge, completed in 1831, and after nearly one hundred and fifty years of service to Londoners transported stone by stone to its new setting at Lake Havasu City, Arizona.

It was in 1968 that the City of London Corporation decided to dispose of the bridge to make way for a new one. They accepted the tender signed by C. V. Wood Jnr on behalf of the McCulloch Oil Corporation and bearing in the space allocated for the amount of their bid the hand-written lettering: 'two million four hundred and sixty-thousand dollars ($2,460,000)'.

Why an oil company would be willing to pay more than a million pounds for an ancient bridge was explained by the fact that the prosperous organization founded by R. P. McCulloch has numerous subsidiaries, one of which is McCulloch Properties Inc., and the bridge was bought for them to build up into a tourist attraction which they hope will rival Disneyland.

At McCulloch Properties Inc. they think big. Not for them property development on the scale of, say, a housing estate or a complex of apartment blocks; they think in terms of building whole cities from scratch. It has been calculated by those who concern themselves with such things that the United States is going to need two hundred new cities by the year 2000. At time of writing McCulloch Properties are engaged in building five of these and look forward in the near future to participating on an even larger scale in helping to cope with America's population explosion.

Cities grow up naturally at a harbour or river mouth at a focal point of sea trade, or inland at places where natural resources are being exploited, or at a location that is central for industry, commerce or government. But when McCulloch's decided arbitrarily to establish the first of their cities-to-be at an abandoned war-time airfield and convalescent centre for servicemen at Lake Havasu, at what was virtually an X on the map, they realized that if it were to grow and prosper it would have to be given some sort of artificial stimulant, something to attract people to that forlorn part of arid Arizona which had little appeal to anyone except asthma sufferers.

What better than what the McCulloch planners termed a 'recreation industry generator'? After all, Disneyland is a recreation industry generator, one of the greatest, and the industry it has generated through people flocking there for recreation has converted the neighbouring sleepy little town into a booming city. Searching around for something to do the same for their projected Lake Havasu City, McCulloch's became excited when London Bridge came on the market.

Who in the English-speaking world, from Aberdeen to Invercargill, from Fiji to California, had not in youth sung the nursery rhyme *London Bridge is Falling Down*? Their researchers came up with the information that the first version of the song had been written in 1014 by Norse poet Ottar Svarte to commemorate the exploit of Viking King Olaf of Norway, who with his fleet rowed up to the timber bridge then spanning the Thames, attached cables to the supporting piles and rowed away, toppling the bridge into the river. Various versions of the song have come into being over the years and the now familiar one was included in the original Mother Goose Rhymes and has become known all over the world.

Anything as readily identified in the public mind as London Bridge would be bound to be a surefire attraction at the new McCulloch city. The fact that there was no river in the area for it to cross (the Colorado being altogether too wide) could be easily overcome by making an artificial waterway for it to span. It could be the centrepiece of the new city, linking the city proper to the airport at which tourists from all over the States and beyond would land, to enjoy the thrill of passing over the legendary London Bridge.

At $2,460,000 (plus carrying charges estimated at $240,000 to get the bridge across the Atlantic) it was an investment that would soon pay dividends as handsome as those at Disneyland.

The deal was done and McCulloch's at once, in Easter 1968, set about the task of shipping London Bridge stone by stone to America, an operation that was to take three and a half years and the like of which had never been undertaken since newspaper magnate Randolph Hearst in the 1920s shipped European antiquities stone by stone across the Atlantic to build his San Simeon retreat.

It is interesting to conjecture what the unostentatious John Rennie would have thought of all the hoop-la surrounding the second opening of his bridge in October 1971, in 'America's new vacation land of Lake Havasu City'. And even more interesting would have been his reaction to the fact that it is not strictly speaking his bridge but merely looks like it. The $2,460,000 the McCulloch organization paid was for 10,000 tons of stone. The Rennie bridge weighed 130,000 tons. The explanation for this discrepancy will emerge in due course.

2 *The Young Rennie*

JOHN RENNIE was born on 7th June 1761 at the farmstead of Phantassie near the town of East Linton, twenty-two miles from Edinburgh. He was the youngest of the nine children of James and Jean Rennie.

In East Linton today the story most often told about Rennie concerns the headmaster of Preston Kirk school, across the valley from Phantassie. Bumping into the boy's father one day he inquired: 'How's young John?'

'He's fine.'

'Oh,' said the headmaster. 'We thought he was ill. He hasn't been to school for three days.'

Apparently this was the perpetual story of the young Rennie. Playing truant was the main feature of his school days. The magnet which drew him away from his regular route to school was the mill and workships of Andrew Meikle, inventor in his own right and the man who perfected the threshing machine. The attraction of the Meikle workshops for young John, mechanically-minded from the time he had become old enough to take note of things around him, is easy to understand. Seeing the forge in action was a joy in itself. Then to be allowed to work the bellows, and at length actually to wield one of the hammers along with the smiths. What dull drudgery was sitting in a classroom compared to that!

As a boy he had a habit of touching one particular stone in the front wall of the farmhouse each day before he went to school, or rather headed in that direction. It was a superstitious action, an outlet for his nervous energy; he felt compelled each morning to press his fingers against the stone, for if he didn't the day would not go well for him. As the years went by the stone became worn away by his touch. Two hundred years later it is still to be seen there.

In his book *The Story of the Bridge*, F. W. Robins has written:

'When Osbert Sitwell was filling in a form and came to the item "Education" he wrote: "While on holidays from Eton." In the same way John Rennie could well have written: "While playing truant from the parish school." '

Meikle took a special interest in the boy, because he soon realized that this was not just a youngster hanging around, getting in the way of people trying to get on with their work. The young lad had a quick grasp of things mechanical. It seemed inborn in him to be an engineer. He was strong enough to work the hammers, even when barely ten, for he had strength beyond his years. Later in life he could lift three hundredweight with his little finger. A close bond grew up between the man and the boy. It was further strengthened by the fact that Rennie's father died when he was five. Meikle was not a rival to his father in the boy's affections. He filled the gap left by the death of Rennie senior.

In his brilliant work, the two-volume *Lives of the Engineers*, published in 1862, Samuel Smiles paints a gloomy picture of the East Lothian area in the days when Rennie was growing up there.

> The art of agriculture, like everything else in Scotland, was in an incredibly backward state, compared with either England or even Ireland. . . . The traveller through the Lothians will scarcely believe that then these districts were not much removed from the state in which nature had left them. In the interior there was little to be seen but bleak moors and quaking bogs. The chief part of each farm consisted of 'out-field' or unenclosed land, no better than moorland, from which even the hardy black cattel could scarcely gather herbage enough to keep them from starving in winter time. The 'in-field' was an enclosed patch of ill-cultivated ground, on which oats and 'bear' or barley were grown; but the principal crop was weeds.
>
> All loads were as yet carried on horseback; but where the farm was too small, or the crofter too poor, to keep a horse, his own or his wife's back bore the load. . . . The implements used in agriculture were extremely rude. They were mostly made by the farmer himself. A plough, made of young birch trees, scratched without difficulty the surface of old crofts, but made sorry work in the out-field, where the sward was tough and stones were large and numerous. Lord Kaimes said of the harrows used in his time, that they were more fitted to raise laughter than to raise mould.
>
> The towns were for the most part collections of thatched mud cottages, giving scant shelter to a miserable population. The whole country was poor, desponding, gaunt, and almost

haggard. The food of the working class was almost wholly vegetable, and even that was insufficient in quantity.

The country was as yet almost without roads, so that communication between one town and another was exceedingly difficult, especially in winter. In wet weather the tracks became mere sloughs, in which the carts and carriages had to slumper through in a half-swimming state, while in time of drought it was a continued jolting out of one hole into another.

The first vehicle which plied between the two chief cities of Scotland was not started until 1749. It was called 'The Edinburgh and Glasgow Caravan', and performed the journey of forty-four miles in two days; but the packhorse continued to be the principal means of communication between the two places. Ten years later another vehicle was started, which was named 'The Fly', because of its extraordinary speed, and it contrived to make the journey in rather less than a day and a half.

The great post-road between London and Edinburgh passed close in front of the house at Phantassie in which John Rennie was born; but even this was little better than the tracks we have already described. It followed the ridge of the Carlton Hills towards Edinburgh. The old travellers had no aversion to hill tops, rather preferring them because the ground was firmer to tread on, and they could see better about them. This line of high road avoided the county town, which, lying in a hollow, was unapproachable across the low grounds in wet weather; and, of all things, swamps and quagmires were then most dreaded.

By the year 1763 this post-road must have been made practical for wheeled vehicles; for in that year the one stage-coach, which for a time formed the sole communication of the kind between London and all Scotland, began to run; and John Rennie, when a boy, was familiar with the sight of the uncouth vehicle lumbering along the road past his door. It 'set out' from Edinburgh only once a month, the journey to London occupying from twelve to eighteen days, according to the state of the roads.

Young Rennie would most certainly have been familiar with the Edinburgh–London coach, for if one goes now to what was once his home one sees that the main road is just a few paces from the house. It is now of course the A1, which takes the passenger in a motor coach down through Newcastle, Yorkshire, the East Midlands and thence to London—in a single day. In actual fact the road as it was in Rennie's time was even closer to the house than the present highway. Standing among the trees in the front garden one can still see indentations in the ground which mark the route of the old road beside which the Rennie boy without doubt used to stand with a sense of excitement at seeing the Edinburgh–London stage coach jolting by.

Having read the Smiles description of the East Lothian country-side as it was some two centuries ago, I approached it with a certain foreboding when I went there to see what still stood of the places where Rennie had spent his youth. Granted, things could have done nothing but improve considerably in the interim, but even so one knows from experience that in a naturally bleak locality even years of improvement of the terrain and amenities cannot completely compensate for basically unattractive country-side.

Thankfully, I was to find that the impression gained from read-ing Smiles is now entirely unrelated to what is a really beautiful part of Scotland.

The railway runs through the town of East Linton but not for the benefit of the local people. Through a Beeching edict trains do not stop in the Lowlands any more; they merely carry people back and forth to England from Edinburgh and Glasgow. So one can go the twenty-two miles from Edinburgh to East Linton only by car or bus: through Musselburgh, over a Rennie bridge across the Esk, to Tranent, Macmerry and Gladsmuir through a landscape of broad vistas of well-tended farms on the long ridges and in the dales—sheep, a crop of sugar-beet, dark rich soil in fields newly ploughed—on to Haddington, the busy county town, past the seat of the Earl of Haddington and thence to East Linton, the Rennie country.

Any of the local people will tell you that if you would explore the Rennie country the best way to do it is to turn off before getting into East Linton and take the by-pass up around the little town in the valley and there on the hill pause to have a look at the Rennie memorial, then on foot follow the slope down to Phantassie House, which is now a mansion, incorporating the original Phantassie farmhouse in its structure. From there go down to the river, to the mill where Rennie lingered on his way to school. Cross the river into the town and finish with a meal at the Harvesters, which has nothing to do with Rennie but which is an inn famed for its food.

So, taking local advice, I stopped off at the Rennie memorial and could see at once that in both concept and execution this structure designed by J. Wilson Paterson, Architect of the Office of Works in the 1920s, is one of the most ghastly monuments ever inflicted on the public. A six-feet-high semi-circle of drab stone, it has a plaque with a likeness of Rennie. In front of it is a bird bath on a pedestal, designed from a relic of his Waterloo Bridge. Set into the stonework are two wooden benches, although why it was thought anyone would want to sit there is a mystery. The memorial stands beside the by-pass that cuts across the open country above East Linton. No one would sit there to wait for a bus, since buses don't go by that route. Only fast-moving cars and transport lorries go by. All one would get from sitting there is the smell of exhaust.

Financed by public subscription in 1928 it had as one of its contributors Herbert Morrison, whom the Labour Party regarded as a great man. Morrison was 'father of the London County Council'. In the controversy about whether or not Rennie's Waterloo Bridge should be demolished when it was found that one of the piers was becoming unsound through the effects of the river, the Labour-dominated LCC was in conflict with the Tories of the Government. The LCC said that the bridge should be pulled down and another built in its place; the Government held the view that, at a fraction of the cost of a new bridge, the weakened pier could be fixed up and the Rennie masterpiece retained. With the argument at its height, the LCC decided to present the Government with a *fait accompli*. They started demolishing the bridge.

In due course when H. B. Amos of Bournemouth, suggested the Rennie memorial and opened a subscription list he received a letter from Morrison. In an item in *The Times*, (headed 'Herbert Morrison's Act of Atonement', Mr Amos said that in his letter the Labour leader had stated that 'when the LCC decided to demolish the old Waterloo Bridge and when he struck the first blow that started the operations he had a sympathetic and respectful thought for Rennie and hoped he would forgive him. In the circumstances he felt he should make a small contribution.'

With no reluctance whatsoever the sightseer in Rennie country turns away from the memorial and walks down from the East Linton by-pass to Phantassie House.

The farmhouse still looks precisely as it did two hundred years ago when Rennie was born and brought up there, with the addition of a wing at each end of its frontage. These additions have been done in greystone and roughcast in perfect character with the original building, so that the whole forms a really impressive country house.

An Edinburgh lawyer is the present owner and he occupies one wing. Other Edinburgh businessmen have taken over proper-

ties in the area and this has brought to East Linton a new lease
of life. The town was once what the guide books describe as 'a
wealthy eighteenth-century burgh' but it has seen a decline over
the years and today by actual count East Linton has only 809
inhabitants. The establishment there of a 'stockbroker belt' would
undoubtedly bring it a new prosperity.

The most interesting thing about the old part of Phantassie—
the original Rennie farmhouse—is the lowness of the ceilings.
One does not need to be very tall to be able to reach up and
touch them. Moving through the house to modern parts one goes
through archways cut into the old walls and can see that they
are three feet thick, of solid stone—a reason why centuries later
the farmhouse stands as firm as it ever did.

On a wall of what is now the house's living-room is an en-
graving of Rennie's time showing the dwelling as it used to be. A
windmill at the back of the house and hayricks at one end are no
longer there and the grazing land up to the front door has now
been replaced by an orderly garden with trimmed hedgerows,
with as a centrepiece a baluster from Rennie's demolished
Waterloo Bridge. From the upper windows of the house one can
look out over the more than six hundred acres of farmland, leased
out now to Thomas Harrison and his family.

Today East Linton cannot help but suffer from the fact that
formerly it was the town centre for two thousand or more people
and now serves a population well under half that. It has that no-
people-around look which has become the fate of so many similar
towns in the Lowlands. One gets the feeling that everything
seems to have stopped around 1880. One of the main impressions
of the English visitor to these areas is that nobody seems to be
building, in contrast to south of the Border, where new houses,
buildings, shops are going up wherever one turns. Visit East
Linton in winter, as I did, and one cannot escape the feeling that
those who still live there are waiting patiently through the winter
months for the coming of the tourists, especially the American
tourists who, fortunately for the locals, seem never to tire of the
desire to see where their forefather came from, whether they be
MacDonalds, McNabs or Macintoshes.

It is a picturesque little town, down in that valley of the Tyne,
not to be confused with that other River Tyne farther south upon
which Newcastle stands, and the town gets its name of Linton
from being on the linn, or rocky cleft in the river. A fourteenth-
century stone bridge spans the linn and you cannot get half-way
across it before you are forced to stop and admire what is a most

wonderful view—out across this miniature gorge to a vista of beautiful Lowland landscape. It comes as no surprise to learn that in the summer this particular spot is a mecca for artists who sit virtually shoulder to shoulder getting it down on canvas.

From what is now called Phantassie House and what was formerly the farmhouse where John Rennie grew up one can retrace his footsteps on his way to school each day. The school was across the valley of the Tyne, and as I walked down the slope from Phantassie the first thing I encountered was a large 'doo'cot', pronounced 'duckit' by the people of East Lothian. There is no question that this doo'cot on young Rennie's route to school was an immediate distraction and represented a pressing invitation to dally.

The centuries-old dovecots of East Lothian are famous. This example in the Phantassie fields is one of twenty or more in the region that have been preserved by the Scottish National Trust. It is open to the public, who can delve around inside, as undoubtedly Rennie did on his way to his lessons two hundred years before. Like a tall redstone windmill, without the sails, the Phantassie dovecot is larger than most, with accommodation for 544 pigeons, but not among the biggest which can house 2,000.

They are somewhat gruesome things, these dovecots. The pigeons used to fly in by the circular hole at the top and were appreciative of the accommodation provided for them—tier upon tier of stone nesting-places, each about the size of a shoe-box, inside thick stone walls away from the wind and the cold. But the idea of providing the pigeons with such good housing was merely to let them fatten up there on the grain they ate in the fields—and then kill them for food.

Before the introduction of turnips and swedes as winter feed for cattle and sheep in the 1700s, the Scots used to slaughter their stock in the autumn and salt the meat for use during the winter months. A steady diet of salted meat can be tedious, so pigeons became a good source of fresh meat, eaten either when the birds were young, as 'squabs', or when older in pigeon pie. The squabs were pronounced particularly delicious and the dovecots were fitted with 'glovers' to prevent the pigeons from fighting among themselves and killing off the young ones. Also there was a course of protecting stones to stop rats from getting at the pigeons before the humans did. All in all, a highly organized way of lulling the poor pigeons into a false sense of security. When dovecots ceased being used is not known for certain. They survive, empty now, perhaps partly because of the tradition that anyone who demolished a dovecot would be dogged by ill luck for the rest of his life.

Having popped into the Phantassie doo'cot to see how the pigeons were coming along, the Rennie boy was undoubtedly already late for school. But another, far bigger temptation was farther along his route. At the bottom of the slope are two foot-bridges over the Tyne, and hard by the first of these is the Houston Mill—Andrew Meikle's mill. Today there is little more than the outer shell of the main building, still in use but not as a mill. However, a few hundred yards downstream is another mill and from this one it is possible to get a very good idea of what the Houston Mill was like in its heyday. The 400-years-old Preston Mill is a wonderful example of an old-time watermill still in perfect working order. It was in fact producing oatmeal and flour up until 1955 and the only reason production stopped then was because that was the year the miller died. Now tourists make special trips there. It is a mecca for artists and photographers. It has been depicted on canvas and in sketch books from every conceivable angle and is without doubt among the most painted ancient watermills in the world. Apart from the old-world charm of the structure and its beautiful setting, the great attraction as far as tourists are concerned is the fact that it still works. National Trust custodian Tom Hunter shows them around and sets the machinery going to give a practical demonstration.

With an old crank handle he opens the sluice gate to release the flow from the weir upstream into the water race. The huge iron wheel on the outside of the mill starts to revolve and inside driving wheels begin turning, conveyor belts go into action, the sifting sieves set up their frenzied agitation, winnowing fans spin, the great grindstones rotate—all of it, the whole ingenious sequence of working machinery, set in motion by the one big wheel outside. Not with the clanging of metal but with the characteristic clumpitty-clump of wooden-toothed driving wheels, the whole building throbs with motion. And then when the custodian swings the sluice gate wide open to allow the full flow down through the water race, one gets the feeling that here indeed is the origin of the expression 'going like the clappers'. But he doesn't give a demonstration very often. 'After all,' he says, 'the old girl's four hundred years old.'

For a grown-up tourist it is fascinating, but how much more so for a youngster like John Rennie, when the machine age was in its infancy. However, this was not the mill at which he lost all track of time and failed to turn up at school. The near-by Houston Mill held far more attraction for him. Not only did it have the same sort of milling operation but in addition there was the presence of Andrew Meikle, more than just a miller—a mill-wright as well, a maker of milling machinery and farming implements, hand-forged wagon wheels and axle trees. And most important of all, a fully-fledged inventor.

Somerset Maugham once said that an author at work on a book is often confronted with a secondary character who becomes so interesting that he bids fair to take over the whole book; in such circumstances, said Maugham, the answer was to take him out of the book and give him one of his own. Such is the case with Andrew Meikle. But pending a Meikle book we could outline his association with and influence on the young Rennie.

Meikle, 'a great man in his own right as a mechanical engineer', had in the middle 1700s greatly advanced the efficiency of wind-mills with his inventions connected with the sails that operated them. This he followed with his invention of the threshing machine (called then a 'thrashing' machine) which he patented in 1788, after developing it from earlier not very effective models evolved by others. He was variously known locally as 'the son of the Devil' and 'the mad inventor', earning these titles partly through his obsessive preoccupation with his machines and partly through having a highly developed sense of humour which was quite beyond the understanding of the simple farm folk of the area.

Once when a woman had come to Meikle with some barley to be milled she waited in an outer room as he started up the grind-stones. In the room were a butter churn, a cradle and several other objects of his manufacture and at the precise moment the milling started these burst into immediate and frenzied activity, apparently quite of their own accord but of course as the result of Meikle having secretly connected them to one of the driving wheels. The woman took to the hills, convinced that evil spirits shared the mill with Meikle.

On another occasion the Earl of Haddington, whose mansion stood on high ground over the River Tyne, mentioned to Meikle that he would dearly like to have what was then the novelty of running water in his home, but of course, being so high up . . . Not at all, said Meikle; he was sure he could fix it for him. To the butler at the Haddington residence this was a vain boast, and he treated Meikle to the sort of lofty disdain that butlers, more than any other beings, are capable of displaying. Meikle went to work and Lord Haddington was indeed provided with what he desired, the butler being the first to get the full benefit of running water in the house—showered on him when he was lying in bed at six o'clock one morning.

While working on a project at Leith, twenty miles from East Linton, Meikle walked each day the forty miles back and forth to the job. At that time he was plagued by what seemed to be insurmountable problems in the working of his prototype of the threshing machine. But one day, walking back from Leith, he came to an abrupt halt in the middle of the road and shouted 'I've got it! I've got it!' He at once went to work sketching out plans with the tip of his walking stick in the dust on the road. It was only when he was satisfied that he had indeed ironed out the snags in his machine that he realized that so intent had he been on thinking about it that he had wandered four miles off the main road back to East Linton and had to retrace his steps.

Another aspect of Meikle's colourful career endeared him to young Rennie. Throughout what was to become known as the Industrial Revolution there are numerous examples of engineers and others using ingenious means to steal ideas from their contemporaries. Twyford, for instance, feigned indifference and stupidity for two years working as a sweeper and cleaner-up in a pottery where some very advanced processes were used in the baking and glazing of chinaware; he memorized all the secret formulas and then set up what is now the flourishing firm of Twyford sanitaryware. The theft of the Bessemer steel secrets was carried out by a man who pretended to be a tramp and pleaded to be allowed to warm himself by the furnaces, and was thus able to make close observation of how it was all done.

Meikle's particular piece of what would be called today industrial espionage was typical of the man. It seems that in his young days there was no way known in Scotland to mill barley efficiently. But Dutch ships coming into Leith brought great sackloads of this commodity and Meikle decided to go over to Holland to find out how they did it. At all the barley mills he went to there he encountered tightly closed doors. One of the millers, however, had a daughter of his age and he set about paying her attentions. In the strict Dutch household there was little opportunity for the two to have any privacy together and Meikle convinced the girl that the thing to do was for her to get the key to the mill and in there, undisturbed, they could further their romance. This she did and as Meikle, the cad, kept her entertained he cast a discerning eye over the mill's machinery. The lovers were discovered. Meikle had to run for it. But he had found out what he wanted to know and he at once took ship back home. And that was how milled barley came to Scotland.

So there, half-way between the Rennie farmstead and the schoolhouse, was this intriguing character Andrew Meikle at work each day at the workshops in the Houston Mill, and soon the mill became more than just a reason for playing truant. When Rennie was twelve he left the school that had seen so little of him and was apprenticed to Meikle. For the next two years he learned the crafts of the carpenter, the stonemason and the blacksmith. He never forgot the debt he owed to Andrew Meikle's training. Throughout his life he kept his old kit of artisan's tools that he had used at the workshops and time and again he would bring them out for use on some job where his workmen were encountering difficulty.

Hard at work at the mill at the age of twelve, Rennie was not a great mixer with the other youngsters in the area. It earned for him a reputation among them of being stand-offish. The simple fact was that his interests were different from theirs. The normal youthful skylarking did not attract him. His serious-minded preoccupation from earliest youth with things mechanical meant that while they were playing he wanted to build something. On at least one occasion, however, he did win favour with the other children. No doubt inspired by the tales of the deeds of Captain Cook and the other great navigators at that time sailing the world to establish the first British Empire, he constructed a fleet of miniature ships. These he launched on the Tyne in spate, to the great delight of the youth of the neighbourhood.

The Phantassie estate had been in the Rennie family for generations and when James had inherited it he married Jean, whose maiden name was also Rennie, in 1743, John was the last born of their children, who were: Marion, born in 1744, Janet in 1745, Jean in 1747, George in 1749, Agnes in 1751, Henrietta in 1753, William in 1756, James in 1758 and John in 1761.

Little is known of Marion Rennie. Second eldest sister Janet, however, had a distinguished descendant. In 1764 she married James Carnegie and a grandson, Andrew Carnegie, migrated to America in 1848, to amass a fortune from iron works and become one of that country's best known philanthropists. Jean Rennie died in infancy. George, eldest of the brothers, will be dealt with more fully later; very capably he took over as head of the family on the death of Rennie senior in 1766. Of Agnes, little is known.

Henrietta was an unhappy soul, a maiden lady who features later in this book, when she served as John Rennie's housekeeper after the death of his wife. Henrietta epitomized the sad fate of the girl who was 'passed over' in that era when the only career for a young lady of good background was marriage. Today she could find compensation in devoting her time to becoming the very capable secretary of a business executive, a highly efficient librarian or one of the better television PRs. But in her time it was unheard of for a girl of quality to go out to work and she had no option but to stay at home and feel sorry for herself. The sexual frustration of her youth became maternal blight as she grew older, childless, in an age when numbering one's children in double figures was something earnestly to be strived for.

Little has been recorded of the life of William, second eldest of the brothers. But it is known that he was taken prisoner while fighting in the American War of Independence and died in captivity in Boston. John Rennie's other brother, James, is mentioned by Samuel Smiles when writing of the more noted member of the family:

James studied medicine at Edinburgh, and entered the army as an assistant-surgeon. The regiment to which he belonged was shortly after sent to India: he served in the celebrated campaign of General Harris against Tippoo Saib, and was killed in 1799 whilst dressing the wound of his commanding officer when under fire at the siege of Seringapatam.

When Rennie senior had died in 1766 John's eldest brother George had taken over as head of the house. Despite the fact that George at the time was a mere seventeen years of age he was capable far beyond his years, either by nature or through necessity. Not only did he conduct family affairs intelligently and shrewdly but he was also to make great improvements in the farm, largely through travels to Berwickshire and other regions where more advanced farming methods had been introduced, applying them in turn to the Rennie holding of six hundred and twenty acres. Eventually the farm was regarded as a model and he was to build for himself a reputation as an agriculturalist as distinguished as that of his younger brother in engineering. His reputation extended overseas and to Phantassie came many distinguished visitors seeking his advice on farming matters, not the least of whom was the Grand Duke Nicholas (afterwards Emperor) of Russia, who stayed several nights at the farmhouse.

George Rennie is buried in the graveyard of Prestonkirk and from the lower fields of the farm one can still see up on the ridge the tall white gravestone which bears a long, well-worded eulogy.

It was in 1773 that John at the age of twelve was taken from the Prestonkirk school and apprenticed to Andrew Meikle. For a boy to be sent off to work at twelve might seem young by modern standards, but not at all for that period, when seven was not regarded as an unreasonable age at which a boy should start making his way in life—on the lower rungs of society, that is. The very fact that young Rennie was twelve before being apprenticed indicated that his family, if not rich, was on a higher social level than the majority in the area.

But after two years in Meikle's workshop the fourteen-year-old Rennie had doubts about the ultimate worth of continuing there. Granted he was getting valuable experience and gaining confidence in the work. Eventually he could set up in business on his own as a millwright but even in his youthful mind he realized that although he would be efficient enough as a craftsman he would find it hard to raise himself above the artisan stage. Accordingly he put his views forward at a family conference and expressed a desire to go to Dunbar High School, out on the coast about six miles from East Linton. The family agreed and he was enrolled there in the autumn of 1775.

At that time, as now, Scotland had a high reputation for the standard of its schooling and an important integral part of the country's educational system was the network of well-run high schools open to anyone of talent. Dunbar High School was well up to the national standard and Rennie found himself in stimulating surroundings in which he made rapid progress. He became head boy and a frequent visitor to the rostrum on prize-giving days.

At one such prize-giving the guest of honour was David Loch, H.M. Inspector General of Fisheries, who happened to be in Dunbar in 1776 at the time when the High School was holding its 'public examinations'. These consisted of leading pupils in English, Latin and Mathematics being questioned by their masters before the assembled parents, prior to being awarded their prizes. In his book *A Tour Through the Trading Towns and Villages of Scotland*, published in 1779, Loch wrote of his visit to Dunbar High School and in a far-seeing passage singled out the young John Rennie for special mention:

Portrait of John Rennie by Sir Henry Raeburn, presented to the Institution of Civil Engineers by his son, Sir John Rennie, in 1849

*Dundas
Aqueduct*

*University of
Manchester*

*Two views of the
Lune Aqueduct*

**University of
Manchester**

Phantassie House as it was
by E. M. Wimperis after a drawing by J. S. Smiles

Phantassie House as it looks now

Mr Gibson, Teacher of Mathematics, afforded a most conspicuous proof of his abilities by his precision and clearness of his manner in stating the questions which he put to his scholars, and their correct and spirited answers to his propositions, and their clear demonstrations of his problems afforded the highest satisfaction and gratification to a numerous audience; and here I must notice in a particular manner the singular proficiency of a young man of the name of Rennie. He was intended for a millwright and was breeding to the business under the famous Andrew Meikle of Linton, East Lothian. He had then attended Mr Gibson for the mathematics not much more than six months, but in his examination he discovered such amazing powers of genius that one would have imagined him a second Newton. No problem was too hard for him to demonstrate with a clear head and decent address and a distinct delivery. His master could not propose a question either in natural or experimental philosophy to which he gave not a clear and ready solution, and also the reason of the connection between cause and effect, the power of gravitation, etc., in a masterly and convincing manner, so that every person present admired such an uncommon stock of knowledge amassed at his time of life. If this young man is spared and continues to prosecute his studies, he will do great honour to his Country.

When he finished his schooling at Dunbar in 1777 young John returned to Phantassie to resume work with Andrew Meikle and continue his studies in his spare time, and one can get a good indication of just how advanced his mathematical ability was from what shortly transpired. His mathematics master at Dunbar, the aforementioned Mr Gibson, was offered the rectorship of the High School at Perth and the question arose of his successor. In the words of Samuel Smiles:

Mr Gibson was pressed by the magistrates to point out some person whom he thought suitable for the office. The only one he could think of was his only pupil; and although not yet quite seventeen years old, he strongly recommended John Rennie to accept the appointment. The young man, however, already beginning to be conscious of his powers, had formed more extensive views of life, and could not entertain the idea of settling down as the 'dominie' of a burgh school, respectable and responsible though that office must be held to be. He accordingly declined the honour which the magistrates proposed to confer upon him, but agreed to take charge of the mathematical classes until Mr Gibson's successor could be appointed. He continued to carry on the classes for about six weeks, and conducted them so satisfactorily that it was matter of much regret when he left the school and returned to his family at Phantassie for the purpose of prosecuting his profession.

Working again with Meikle, he found him very much pre-occupied with his invention of the threshing machine which at this time was nearing completion. As a result Meikle delegated much of his work to his young assistant. Out on his own on jobs such as repairing corn-mills, some of them a considerable distance away so that he could not easily refer to Meikle, young Rennie found himself having to make his own decisions. His self-reliance and confidence developed. At eighteen he was undertaking work on his own account, the first purely Rennie job being the design-ing of Know Mill on the Phantassie estate for his brother George. By then brother George, in his thirties, was a farmer of high standing, and other commissions came through his contacts. Also Meikle passed on to him assignments he was too busy to undertake himself. Early in 1780, at nineteen years of age, he was tackling a really big project farther afield, the fitting up of the mills at Invergowrie, near Dundee, today a relatively easy seventy miles up across the Firth of Forth but at that time a hazardous journey inland and out again of more than a hundred and twenty miles. Before the end of 1780 he had more work coming his way than he could handle.

However, by being a successful millwright before he was twenty he did not feel that he had reached a goal. It was merely a step-ping stone to bigger things. The books he pored over at night at Phantassie were not enough. He would have to have broader studies in science and mathematics if he was going to keep faith with his ambitions. Fatherless since he was five, he could talk his future over with his mother, with his elder brother George and with Andrew Meikle. His mother was no great influence on his life. She remained at all times a shadowy figure. Little is recorded about her and it is not even known definitely when she died, although it appears to have been some time in the late 1790s. He confided mainly in George and Meikle and when he expressed a wish to go to the University of Edinburgh they were completely in favour. But one thing the dedicated young man made abun-dantly clear was that if he did go he would not, during his univer-sity years, be a burden on the family.

Unlike many university students Rennie worked his way through college. From the time of his enrolment in November

1780, through the next three years he paid for his tuition and his keep in Edinburgh by work done during each long vacation from May to September, which by happy coincidence was the busy time for engineers.

Rennie was fortunate in taking classes under two extremely good men—Dr Joseph Black, Professor of Chemistry, and Dr John Robison, Professor of Natural Philosophy. Dr Black (1728–1799) is known today for his discoveries in chemistry, particularly of carbon dioxide and latent heat. His original work earned him the title of the father of quantitative chemistry. But it was Dr Robison who was to have the more profound influence upon Rennie, not only at the university but later in his life. Robison (1739–1805) made numerous contributions to the science of electricity and to other spheres of physics. He was exceptional at applying theory to the practical uses of everyday affairs and this he called Mechanical Philosophy, a term which appears in the title of more than one of the books he wrote. He was a spectacular teacher. His appearance alone commanded attention. A pigtail dangling from his large head to such length that it reached far down his back, he wore doublet and blue worsted hose, out-of-doors on his walks as well as in the lecture room. He had a great sense of humour and was a lively talker. He liked nothing better than engaging in animated discussion with his students, who found him a brilliantly stimulating imparter of knowledge.

Rennie did not graduate from Edinburgh, since he took several specialized science subjects rather than the full course. His time there was invaluable to him in his work. Unlike most of the engineers of his time he could not only bring practical experience to the design of structures but also apply scientific theory from his university studies. Later in life he was to look on his years at Edinburgh as among the most profitable and instructive in his life.

On leaving the university in 1783 he decided to set off on his version of the Grand Tour. Not for him the customary journey down through Paris to Venice, Florence and Rome to view the architectural glories and antiquities. A much more intriguing prospect for him was the idea of a trip down into England to see some of the exciting things being done in bridge-building, canal construction and the developing of radically new machinery by the inventive engineers of the time.

In those days, indeed through to Victorian times, it was a usual thing for the young man of ambition to 'tramp', to go on foot from town to town looking for work or in search of broader scope for his talents. But Rennie, through his profitable employment during his summer holidays, had not only been able to finance his university education. He had surplus funds. He could do his trip on horseback, with money in his pocket.

So, in the summer of 1783 he headed south towards Birmingham, which was already firmly established as the focal point for workers in metal and makers of machinery. At Soho, on the outskirts of the city, James Watt had his workshops, and Rennie was armed with a letter of introduction from Dr Robison.

On his leisurely route, stopping off to have a closer look at anything that captured his interest, he made an examination of work in progress on Thomas Harrison's bridge over the River Lune, just outside Lancaster, with no way of knowing that some years later he was going to design and build a much more ambitious structure across the river no great distance away. The Duke's Canal', that vast project of subterranean waterways conceived by the Duke of Bridgewater for the haulage of coal across Lancashire to the Mersey docks, was under construction and Rennie stopped off at Worsley, headquarters of the undertaking. He was not, it seems, as impressed as other visitors, being of the opinion that the whole thing could have been carried through in different fashion and at much less cost. He looked over Thomas Speer's floating dock at Liverpool where he himself was to be engaged in extensive dock construction in the not-too-distant future.

At all times the young tourist had with him a notebook in which he would jot down details of things seen, plus his observations and as often as not drawings of various aspects of buildings and bridges. Out-of-doors, in those days long before fountain pens and ballpoints, he would make his original notes in pencil (or more probably a graphite stick), to be inked over with a quill pen at night in his lodgings. These notebooks still survive and one can see in them his painstaking regard for detail and his incisive style of comment.

At length arrived at the Soho works, Birmingham, he was received in friendly manner by Watt, who had been at Glasgow University with Professor Robison. This first meeting with Watt was to lead to an association between the two men which lasted until the death in 1819 of the genius of the steam engine. We go into detail about their relationship in a later chapter. For the moment suffice it to say that Watt showed him as much of his work as he felt he should be allowed to see and the young man then set off back home to Scotland.

He at once became immersed in numerous commissions which had been hanging fire during his England trip and now for the first time he was to venture outside his usual work of designing and erecting mills. In 1784 the trustees of the county of Mid-Lothian commissioned him to build a bridge across the Water of Leith, about two miles west of Edinburgh on the Glasgow road. This was his first bridge, the start of the career of Rennie the bridge-builder.

3 *The Albion Mills*

THE name of John Rennie was first brought to public attention with the building of the Albion Mills in 1784. He had only just turned twenty-three when he embarked on the project.

The building of a flour mill seems a prosaic sort of way to make oneself known to the public but the Albion enterprise was something quite revolutionary, not only as regards milling but also in regard to the construction of machinery, and upon its completion in 1788 was regarded as 'one of the wonders of the world'.

Before that time, milling had progressed slowly from the ancient, laborious hand grinding to windmills and the use of water power, as with the Preston and Houston mills of Rennie's youth. But with the wind- and water-mills the development of methods of milling remained static for centuries. Nobody appeared to give a thought to making more efficient something that seemed satisfactory enough and certainly nobody thought 'big'. The local miller providing for the wants of his neighbourhood seemed a good enough arrangement.

However, James Watt and his partner Matthew Boulton in the 1770s started to look towards flour milling as a field in which their steam engine could be put to good use. Previously it had been used mainly in the drainage of mines. Knowing nothing about the practical side of milling they had got together with various millwrights and attempts were made to harness steam power to the production of flour. These early experiments were not entirely successful, mainly because the millwrights were set in their ways and thought in terms of the wooden cogged machinery that did service for the limited power of the water wheel but which was sorely tested by the new, ferocious and so often unpredictable demon that Watt had brought forth.

When the firm of Boulton and Watt got the contract to provide the power for the projected Albion Mills, Watt felt that for the building of the milling machinery he must turn to someone who not only had the millwright's skill but also more vision than the men he had been working with. Watt in fact was almost driven crazy by the endeavours of the well-meaning millwrights he employed. He wrote to partner Boulton:

> Our millwrights have kept working, working at the corn-mill ever since you went away, and it is not yet finished; but my patience being exhausted, I have told them it must be at an end to-morrow, done or not done. There is no end of millwrights once you give them leave to set about what they call machinery; here they have multiplied wheels upon wheels until it has now almost as many as an orrery.[1]

There are two versions of how Rennie came to be the man to whom, in desperation, Watt and Boulton turned. Rennie's son John was to write:

> In connection with the Albion Mills, Boulton & Watt were entrusted with the task of fitting out the mill. Not knowing much about milling machinery they wrote to Dr Robison to recommend someone, as Scotland was famous for millwrights then; and he recommended John Rennie to them.

The other version is that Watt had remembered the great talents Rennie had shown during the young man's visit to his Soho works in 1783 and wrote to Dr John Robison, professor of Natural Philosophy at Edinburgh University, asking whether he would back his (Watt's) judgment in taking on an engineer so young and relatively inexperienced, to which Robison's reply was entirely satisfactory.

In any event, letters were exchanged between Watt and Rennie's mentor in Edinburgh and the upshot was that the budding engineer was summoned to Birmingham and offered the job. Rennie accepted and started off to London to be on the spot to start work from scratch.

The London that Rennie was to find himself in on this first sojourn that was to lead to his permanent establishment there was not in a very happy state. In the middle 1780s the whole country was in a serious depression as a consequence of the unsuccessful ending of the American War of Independence. Parliament was in the process of defraying the heavy cost of the struggle with the colonies and the people were discontented about the increase of

---

[1] A contrivance showing the relative motions of the solar system by means of balls moved by clockwork driven wheels, named after its inventor, the Earl of Orrery (1676–1731).

debt and taxes. Local government and the police were most inefficient—the 'peelers' of Sir Robert Peel's new police service were
not to come into being until 1829. Just before Rennie's arrival
London had, during the Gordon 'No-Popery Riots', been in
the hands of the rioters and blackened ruins still marked their
progress through the city. Although London was the largest city
in Europe the population was barely a million, but even at that
it was thought so large as to be unmanageable. Its northern
boundary was at Hick's Hill, Clerkenwell. Camden Town was as
yet green fields and Kensington, Bermondsey, Marylebone and
Chelsea were outlying villages. Fields and hedgerows led to the
hills of Highgate and Hampstead. The West End of London was
a sparsely inhabited suburb, the building of Fitzroy Square not
being begun until 1793. The most westerly living quarters of
Westminster were at Millbank, with a wide tract of marshy
ground extending opposite Lambeth. Executions were still being
conducted in Tyburn field. Oxford Street had merely a few houses
on the north side. Pennant, the eighteenth-century traveller and
writer, wrote:

> I remember it as a deep hollow road and full of sloughs, with
> here and there a ragged house the lurcking place of cut-throats;
> insomuch that I was never taken that way by night, in my
> hackney-coach, to a worthy uncle's who gave me lodging at his
> house in George Street, but I went in dread the whole way.

Paddington was 'in the country' and the communication with it
was kept up by means of a daily stage—a lumbering vehicle,
driven by its proprietor—which was heavily dragged into the city
in the morning, down Gray's Inn Lane, with a rest at the Blue
Posts, Holborn Bars, to give passengers an opportunity of doing
their shopping. The morning journey was performed in two hours
and a half, 'quick time', and the return journey in the evening in
about three hours.

To this London came John Rennie in 1784 and the site for the
Albion Mills having been decided upon he took lodgings nearby,
in Stamford Street, Southwark, following the London custom of
the time (and for at least a century afterwards) of living, if not
actually on the job, at least adjoining it, for the obvious transport
reasons indicated above. The building site was on the river, hard
by the eastern side of the south approach to Blackfriars Bridge.
Today Londoners who commute by car leave their vehicles there
in a public car park that bears no sign that the spot has a history.
This location for the Albion Mills was chosen for two main

Preston Mill

Houston Mill

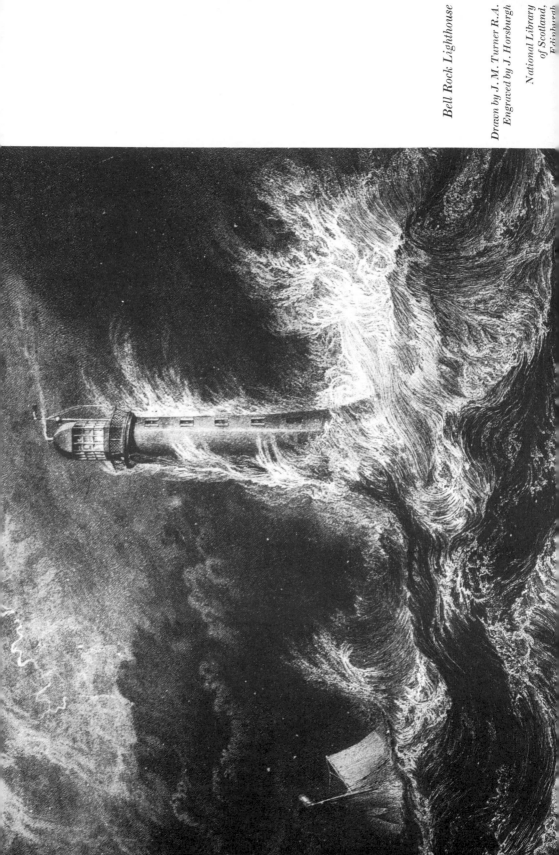

Bell Rock Lighthouse

Drawn by J. M. Turner R.A.
Engraved by J. Horsburgh

National Library
of Scotland,
Edinburgh

reasons. One was the handy supply of abundant water for what were originally called Watt's 'fire engines'. The other was the convenient transit for the grain coming in and the flour going out. There were no public docks on the Thames at that time, only a few private ones of limited extent. Execution Dock at Wapping was not, of course, a dock in the accepted sense but the scene of the despatch of criminals, who were hanged by a gallows at low-water mark, their dead bodies to be cut loose and carried away on the next out-going tide. The smaller trading vessels came right up the Thames to discharge direct at the wharves and warehouses on the banks of the river; larger ships lay farther down near the estuary, waiting for lighters to go back and forth with their cargoes.

The outward structure of the six-storey mill was designed by Samuel Wyatt, brother of the more celebrated James, and an ingenious feature of it was that the river transport went literally right into the building. There were no external quays or landing stages. Built flush with the river bank, there was an arched opening through which the lighters could go in under the mill to a basement lagoon where loading and unloading could take place not only expeditiously but also unhampered by adverse weather conditions outside.

The building was to house two of the largest and most powerful steam engines yet built in Watt's Soho 'manufactory', and it was Rennie's function to design and construct all the milling machinery to be powered by these two engines—for a young man in his early twenties, quite an undertaking. And it is a tribute to his genius that almost a hundred years later engineers could still say of it that it was 'one of the best pieces of that class of engineering ever constructed, either before or since, and performed a quantity of work to the proportion to the power employed such as has never been surpassed'.

In technical terms, Smiles wrote of the millworks:

They consisted of two double-acting engines, of the power of 50 horses each, with a pressure of steam of five pounds to the superficial inch—the two engines, when acting together, working with the power of 150 horses. They drove twenty pairs of millstones, each four feet six inches in diameter, twelve of which were usually worked together, each pair grinding ten bushels of wheat per hour, by day and night if necessary. The two engines working together were capable of grinding, dressing &c., complete, 150 bushels an hour—by far the greatest performance achieved by any mill at that time, and probably not since surpassed, if equalled. But the engine power was also applied to a diversity of other purposes, then altogether novel—such as hoisting and lowering the corn and flour, loading and unloading the barges, and in the process of fanning, sifting and dressing —so that the Albion Mills came to be regarded as among the greatest mechanical wonders of the day. The details of these various ingenious arrangements were entirely worked out by Mr Rennie himself.

It certainly brings the Industrial Revolution into perspective when one realizes that the most important aspect of Rennie's achievement at the Albion Mills, the thing that brought old-time engineers such as Telford and Smeaton there to marvel, was that the machinery's driving shafts, gears and so on were made of metal. Today with metal machinery to be seen at every turn, from factories in the cities to harvesters in the fields, it is hard to realize that until Rennie's innovation the working parts of flour mills, textile mills and all other large mechanical projects were pro- pelled with wooden gearing. The fact that the wooden teeth of a driving wheel did not make a snug fit with the cogs of its neighbour meant that the full driving force was lost. The sliding around of the component parts produced a high percentage of friction and a further wastage of power.

Certain engineers had used metal in a limited way, with iron castings bolted to the wooden driving wheels. Rennie rethought it all. Why not cast the whole thing in iron? And why not, by means of chipping and filing, have the cogs fitting snugly, so that each would be exerting its maximum driving pressure and friction would be reduced to a minimum? This seems obvious to us now but in the 1780s Rennie was the first to do it. His machinery at the Albion Mills formed the model for future engineers to work by— long in advance of the Iron Age of the Victorian engineers (Brunel and company) who are regarded as the pioneers in this field but who in fact merely followed where Rennie had led.

Only in certain working parts at the Mills, and solely to reduce the noise factor, did Rennie keep faith with the tradition of wooden gearing. And this he was to regret.

From their opening on 4th February 1788 the Albion Mills were an immediate financial success, being kept at maximum production from the outset. The output was prodigious by the standards of the time. For example, in June 1790, Boulton reported enthusi- astically to Watt that £6,800 worth of flour was ground in one week. It became a showplace, not only for engineers and others technically minded, but also the general sightseer in London.

But one day in the spring of 1791—Rennie felt unaccountably ill at ease. A presentiment of calamity hung on him but he was at a loss to fathom why or give any explanation of his foreboding to his friends. In his Stamford Street house just a short distance from the mills he went to bed early but had great difficulty in getting to sleep. When he did doze off he awoke with a start having dreamt that the mills were on fire. He got up and looked out, but all was quiet. He went back to bed and was eventually able to get properly to sleep only to be woken up abruptly by shouts of 'Fire!' out in the streets and the rumble of fire-engines. He hurriedly got dressed and rushed out, across the approach to Blackfriars Bridge to a blaze that was filling the night sky with a glow that had attracted people from miles around. His great work, the Albion Mills, was engulfed in flames and although he went to work with the firemen it was a quite hopeless task. The mills were burnt to the ground beyond hope of any sort of repair, and they were never rebuilt.

The cause of the fire was never definitely established. It seemed obvious to many that it was the work of an incendiary. The erection of the mills had been viewed with hostility from various quarters. Workers saw it heralding automation on a huge scale and thus as a threat to their livelihood. The small millers saw it as a danger to their existence. They played up the accusation of monopoly, coupled with the contention that such monopoly could only bring price-rigging in its wake and resultant higher prices of the people's staple food supply. The price of flour had in fact gone up shortly after the opening of the mill and the directors of the Albion Mills Company had to defend themselves in a pamphlet they published in which they maintained that it was solely an increase in the cost of wheat that had forced flour prices up, the mill having actually reduced the average milling cost from 5s. 0¾d. to 3s. 4d. per sack. Nevertheless there was a growing hatred of the mill among certain elements and arson seemed a logical explanation for what had happened on the night of 3rd March 1791.

But the irony was that Rennie, delving in the ruins of his iron-made masterpiece, came up with what he felt was the cause of the fire. He came to the conclusion that in a section where he *had* used wood, the large corn-dressing machine, a wooden bearing had run hot and started it all.

4 *Watt and Rennie*

WHEN one reads biographies of James Watt he comes through as a decent enough person in his dealings with people; but when one reads the lives of men who had dealings with him one wonders whether this was in fact true.

When Watt got Rennie to design and build the machinery incorporating his steam engines at the Albion Mills, Rennie started by spending two months at Watt's workshops at Soho, Birmingham. The idea was that the young engineer would familiarize himself with the engines that were to supply the power for his machines but his observations were so astute that Watt saw in him a future rival in the field of steam power. Accordingly, before Rennie set forth to London to commence work on the mills Watt produced a written agreement which he asked him to sign. The opening section of the document contained an undertaking that Rennie would 'abstain from interfering with the steam engines' during and after installation at the mills. That was fair enough. But quite amazing and a very revealing insight into the character of James Watt was the clause that followed. Rennie was asked to agree that he would refrain from executing any work on steam engines 'upon his own account at any future period'.

Watt, twenty-five years older than the then twenty-three-year-old Rennie, might have thought that the young man might be sufficiently in awe of him to sign such an undertaking. But Rennie would have none of it. He said in effect that Mr Watt could have his steam engine and that he would concentrate on other things. It was a verbal agreement Rennie adhered to. Throughout his career he never undertook any original work on steam engines. Even when later in life part of the function of his own extensive workshops was the building of machinery for ships he farmed out the actual making of the steam power units.

Watt's jealous attention to the great capabilities of young Rennie went beyond merely the fear of his invading his territory.

Watt was extremely critical of Rennie's whole approach to his work. The epitome of what Americans call a man who 'plays it close to the chest', Watt was ever cautious and suspicious of anyone showing interest in what he was doing. Rennie by contrast liked to enjoy the satisfaction of a job well done and was only too pleased to let people see at close quarters the results of his efforts. Therefore, when the Albion Mills started production Watt was horrified to learn that Rennie was showing all sorts of people over the place. He wrote to Boulton:

> It has given me the utmost pain to hear of the many persons who have been admitted into the Albion Mills merely as an Object of Curiosity.... R. no doubt has vanity to indulge as well as us, but he should be curbed and the bad consequences pointed out to him, it will ruin him, Dukes and Lords and noble peers will not be his best customers.

In the final event Watt proved to be very wide of the mark in his final assertion. But this basic difference in attitude towards their respective innovations is interesting. Should one go to the greatest, almost obsessional lengths in safeguarding one's work from prying eyes? Or should one be quite open about it? A short answer is that today Watt's name is known in every corner of the world. Rennie's is not.

Watt always hastened to register at the Patent Office any and every new idea he got, whether it were of major importance or merely a small modification of something already patented. However, one invention of far-reaching importance which is attributed to him he never patented—the centrifugal governor, the device used so extensively today for regulating the speed of an engine.

How Watt presented this boon to the mechanical world with his drawing of its specifications made on 13th December 1788, makes an intriguing story.

Apparently when Boulton in London had made one of his periodic inspections of work in progress at the Albion Mills he wrote to Watt in Birmingham telling him how impressed he was with something he had seen there—the application of a governor to a steam-engine to regulate its motion automatically. He went into detail about the device in his letter. H. W. Dickinson in his biography of Watt writes:

> This was all that was necessary for Watt's acute mind. Five months later, in the firm's 'Drawings Day Book', recording work

done in the drawing office, we have an entry under November 8th, of a 'Drawing of centrifugal engine regulator for no. of strokes'. On December 11th, Southern started a new drawing which he finished and dated '13th Dec. 1788'. This notable drawing shows that heavy balls, two in number, are attached by link-work to a vertical shaft so that, when the speed increases, they fly outwards under centrifugal action, and in doing so raise a sleeve which by a lever actuates a butterfly or throttle valve in the steam pipe leading to the engine. The supply of steam is thereby diminished and the speed of the engine consequently reduced till equilibrium is again established. Watt did not patent the governor.[1]

The reason is obvious. He stole the idea from Rennie. Rennie's tendency to leave his inventions lying around, so to speak, resulted in his not being given the credit by future generations for being the creator of numerous mechanical devices which are commonplace today. Not for him the honour of having his name incorporated in the language without a capital letter, as with the bunsen burner, macadam roads, the diesel engine and so on.

Despite Watt's contention that Rennie 'no doubt had his vanity to indulge' he was not at pains to see to it that everybody knew that it was he, John Rennie, who had developed this new idea or that improvement to an existing mechanism. Dedicated to making his bridges and other constructions stand the test of time and his machines perform with the maximum efficiency, Rennie would develop just as part of his everyday work things which other engineers would regard as inventions.

As a perfect example of this take ball-bearings, which today are such an important, but taken for granted, component of anything from the humble bicycle to the most sophisticated aero engine. On the basis that revolvers developed by Samuel Colt are called 'colts', ball-bearings should rightfully be called 'rennies', for John Rennie perfected their use for the reduction of friction between moving parts.

By coincidence, almost at exactly the same time that Rennie did this (1791), another Britisher put small metal balls to another specialized use and was incorporated into the language as a common word. Lieutenant (later General) Henry Shrapnel of the British Army got the idea of encasing musket balls in an artillery shell, to be lethally scattered on explosion as 'shrapnel'. Doubtless he received lasting credit—if credit is the right word

[1] *James Watt: Craftsman & Engineer* by H. W. Dickinson (Cambridge University Press, 1936).

—because what he did had more dramatic impact on the public mind.

Rennie used ball-bearings when he was required to build numerous swing-bridges over the fifty-seven mile Kennet and Avon Canal linking the Severn and the Thames. At that time the swing-bridge, usually of wood, was a cumbersome affair, difficult for bargees or others to mandhandle out of the way to allow the passage of traffic on the canal and invariably requiring the services of the barge horses. Rennie gave the bridge a much smoother, less demanding swing by setting it on a circular metal race containing four-inch balls. Five years later, in 1796, when building the Lancaster Canal, he issued instructions for the swing bridges to be constructed with ball-bearings 'like those I used on the Kennet and Avon Canal'. This considerably pre-dates what the *Dictionary of National Biography* claims to be the first use of ball bearings, by Robert Stevenson in the cranes in Bell Rock Lighthouse, which was completed in 1811.

Could it truthfully be said, then, that Rennie *invented* ball-bearings? As Professor Joad would have put it, it all depends what you mean by invent. Marconi is identified in the public mind as the 'inventor' of wireless, whereas his apparatus for sending wireless messages was merely the culmination of experiments that had been conducted for many years by numerous other men besides himself. In other words he made it work, he brought it into practical, efficient operation; just as James Watt, 'inventor of the steam engine', earned that title merely through making a radical improvement in 1769 to the steam engines of Papin (1690), Savery (1698) and Newcomen (1712).

Rennie put ball-bearings to effective use in his swing bridges when nobody else had done so before. He adapted them to many other uses. So did numerous other engineers. Perhaps it is only because there is very little about ball-bearings to capture the public imagination that this important contribution by Rennie has claimed little attention.

A problem confronted by all inventors, and something which once prompted Watt to comment 'of all things in life there is nothing more foolish than inventing', is that later generations take for granted devices which seem so obvious in their function that they never needed actually to be invented. Putting a rubber on the end of a pencil, for example, is such an obvious thing to do that it is hardly worth a second thought. But the point is that pencils may have existed for many, many years before someone, name unknown, came up with that bright idea.

The same applies to the gantry crane. With so many of these to be seen today one would think that it did not require much thought to evolve what is technically known as 'a large, bridge-like frame structure carrying a travelling crane'. But up to the early part of last century nobody had actually thought of it. Although no etymologist has been able to find the derivation of the word 'gantry' (or 'gauntry' as sometimes used) this type of crane was first seen when Rennie was at work on building additions to the West India Docks in 1820 and 'erected the apparatus for raising heavy blocks of mahogany'. Even by 1875 the gantry crane was enough of a novelty for his son, Sir John, to write that it 'has been since very generally employed in almost all building operations'.

Rennie's gantry crane was an adaptation of an apparatus he had developed in 1806 when constructing Ramsgate Harbour. He had built out over the water 'a scaffold to which were attached movable trucks with windlasses on a railway for raising and lowering the diving-bell'.

The diving-bell itself was a revolutionary method of working under water. 'The diving-bell', wrote his son John, 'may almost be said to have been an invention of his, for he effected such improvements in it.' Smeaton had used one for laying down moorings and removing obstacles on the sea bed. Rennie's development rendered it 'for the first time applicable to building masonry under water with as much security and accuracy as building upon dry land'. The one used at Ramsgate was of cast iron and weighed five tons. For vision for the workmen glass bulls-eyes were inserted. Fresh air was supplied through a two-and-a-quarter-inch hose pipe. Stones for the foundations of the quays and other under-water masonry were lowered separately and there were controls inside the bell for the masons to work the chains attached to these.

All in all, the Rennie diving bell was far less trouble and much more economic than the building of coffer-dams for extensive under-water work. Such a tremendous advance in this field gave rise to a great deal of interest and much copying by other engineers and was a striking example of the far-reaching scope of Rennie's inventiveness.

Many of his revolutionary developments are far too technical to be touched upon in this book, being concerned with structural theory, equilibrium of arches and complicated aspects of hydraulic as well as mechanical engineering. His insight into and practical application of these things was such that when his professor at Edinburgh University, Dr Robison, was commissioned to write the articles on Mechanics for the third edition of the *Encyclopaedia Britannica* in 1793 he made the trip down to London to consult his pupil, unashamedly admitting that he was making the journey so that he might 'extract as much information from him as possible'.

5 *The Slayer of Dragons*

THERE is a long broad stretch of the English countryside running north from the Thames Estuary—through Essex, Suffolk, Norfolk and Lincoln—which many people regard as the less beautiful part of the country. Unlike the usual hills and dales of picture-postcard England it is flat. Granted, holiday-makers enjoy their summer fortnights in boats on the Norfolk Broads or at seaside resorts along the coast, and the Royal Family have a residence at Sandringham where they forgather at the New Year. But by and large the miles and miles of flat landscape have a great lack of appeal for the average Englishman. However, if it looks unattractive now it is nothing compared to its dreary aspect in Rennie's day. And it is thanks to him and the other men who worked on the draining of the Fens that at least now the depressing vista of flooded land has been replaced by fertile crop-producing fields and market gardens.

In view of the work he did in land drainage in Lincolnshire and other parts of the eastern seaboard of England, Rennie earned for himself the title of 'the greatest slayer of dragons that ever lived'. To those who lived there he was a great benefactor, his work doing so much to rid them of the evils that emanated from the swampland—the sickness and disease that had been known from ancient times as the dragons of the Fens.

In 1789 Rennie's attention had been drawn to what was called 'the drowned state of the rich low-lying lands to the south of Ely'. Despite large-scale pioneer work by such men as Cornelius Vermuyden as far back as the early 1600s, vast areas of good arable soil in Lincoln and neighbouring counties lay unprofitably under water. Such a region was the fifty thousand acres of the Soham and Bottesham Fens south of Ely. Even such parts as could be used for farming were alluded to as 'rotten land', because of the foot-rot which infected the sheep put out to graze.

Rennie made a survey and decided that the most efficient way to clear the water would be to set up a pumping station making use of one of Watt's steam engines. Apart from its use in the Albion Mills, the Watt engine, patented in 1769, was in this period thought of mainly in connection with mining operations, so that when Rennie got in touch with Watt regarding a suitable engine for land drainage and included one in his specifications for the clearing of the Soham and Bottesham Fens, the authorities felt that he was being altogether too much of a visionary. To them a drainage scheme was not something which should incorporate a new-fangled thing like the Watt steam engine; drainage should be done as it had always been done, by Vermuyden and other Dutchmen brought over to try to cope with the situation, by the use of windmills imported from Holland.

It is interesting that the opposition to his new ideas that Rennie encountered was precisely the sort of thing Vermuyden had come up against with his windmills. He had found that there was much superstitious prejudice against 'artificially created wind'. Some ministers argued that it was irreligious of man 'to raise wind for himself and by efforts of his own'. More than one minister refused holy communion to those of his congregation who thus irreverently raised 'the Devil's wind'. In his novel *Old Mortality* Sir Walter Scott made an allusion to this in his description of Mause Headrigg's indignation when it was proposed that

Cuddie should work in the barn wi' a new-fangled machine for dightin' the corn free frae the chaff, thus impiously thwarting the will of Divine Providence by raising wind for your leddyship's ain particular use by human art, instead of soliciting it by prayer, or waiting patiently for whatever dispensation of wind Providence was pleased to send upon the shealing-hill.

However, with the people of the Fens now wedded to this windmill, Rennie could not budge them on their attitude towards steam power. His scheme for the drainage of the fifty thousand acres of the Soham and Bottesham Fen was shelved. But just how far ahead of his time he was in this, as in so many other things, is indicated by the fact that more than thirty years later, in 1820, he was called in again and asked to go ahead with his scheme. And even by then it was the first time a steam engine had been put to such work. The pumping station was highly successful and others then turned to drainage by this system, not only in England but also in Holland, where they copied it in preference to their windmills.

Rennie's most important work in this field, however, was his draining of some seventy-five thousand acres of land lying immediately south of Lincoln, an area stretching from near the Nottinghamshire border across to the Wash and including the Wildmore Fen, West Fen and East Fen. What was in those days described as 'the vapoury climate of Britain' had this district under water for most of each year. Valuable land was made useless for tillage or grazing and the only worthwhile crop were the tall reeds used for the thatched roofs of cottages and barns. The river Witham, on which Lincoln stands, flows through the middle of this area and at that time it had become so silted up that in numerous places there was the unusual situation of the bed of the river being above the level of the ground on either side. Not unnaturally, flooding of the Witham was a regular occurrence and it was remarked that 'there were not two houses in the whole parish of Dogdyke communicable with each other for whole winters except by boat, this being the only means by which the fen-slodgers could get to church'. It was a miserable existence for the poor fen-slodgers, huddled in their reed huts or living in sodden boats, praying to God that they would survive onslaughts of that old-sounding ailment the ague, which on investigation turns out to have been a corruption of *acute* fever brought on by 'malaria' in its original meaning of bad odours from the swamps.

The East Fen, being on a lower level than the West and Wildmore Fens, got the full brunt of their overflow and was by far the worst off. A big landowner in the area was Sir Joseph Banks. From his country seat of Abbot's Lodge at Revesby, which was needless to say on high ground, he had an extensive view of that part of 'the moist county of Lincoln' and it was he who bestirred other wealthy landowners to join him in getting something done about the situation.

Sir Joseph Banks the naturalist was one of the most eminent men of his time. He was born in London of a Lincolnshire family in 1743 and performed the neat trick of going to both Eton and Harrow. As a boy he revealed his great interest in botany, and when on holidays in the country he would pay flower-pickers at the market gardens sixpence for each important piece of information they could give him. When he was at Oxford his father died and he inherited the family fortune and several estates. At twenty-five he went with Captain Cook on his voyage to the South Seas in the *Endeavour* to collect botanical specimens, and from Port-Royal Bay, Tahiti, he observed the transit of Venus. On subsequent voyages to various parts of the world he amassed valuable botanical collections which he bequeathed to the British Museum. He was president of the Royal Society and was accused of despotism, a criticism not easy to avoid in view of the fact that he held the post for forty-two years until his death at seventy-seven in 1820.

But even if certain Fellows of the Royal Society might have thought him autocratic, he was very popular with other people he met outside London during time spent regularly each year not only at Revesby but at each of his other country mansions. He was pronounced jolly and good-humoured and although a distinguished man, not above taking part in the general goings-on and festivities in the neighbourhood where he resided. A frequent guest at Abbot's Lodge wrote:

When Sir Joseph lived at Revesby he used to keep almost open house and a constant succession of visitors came and went—some on pleasure, some on friendship and some on business. The profuse hospitality of the place was enjoyed not less by the postillions and grooms who drove thither the baronet's guest's than by the visitors themselves; and it was esteemed by the hotel postboys a great privilege to drive a customer to Revesby. On one occasion, when Mr Rennie was to dine and sleep at the Lodge, he took an opportunity of saying to the principal butler that he hoped he would see to his postboy being kept *sober*, as he wished to leave before breakfast on the following morning. The butler replied, with great gravity, that he was sorry he could not oblige Mr Rennie, as the same man had left Revesby sober the last time he was there, but only on condition that he might be allowed to get drunk the next time he came. 'Therefore', said the butler, 'for the honour of the house, I must keep my word; but I will take care that you are not delayed for the want of horses and another postboy.' The butler was as good as his word; the man got drunk, the honour of Revesby was saved, and Mr Rennie was enabled to set off in due time next morning.

Sir Joseph missed no opportunity of trying to interest anyone he thought could be helpful in his scheme to reclaim the vast stretches of drowned land that could be seen from the front terrace of Abbot's Lodge. Early in 1799 Arthur Young wrote in his *Report on Lincolnshire* that 'he would not let his favourite topic rest until he had ordered a boat, and accompanied me into the heart of East Fen, which had the appearance of a chain of lakes, bordered by great crops of reed'.

Sir Joseph was a public-spirited man and his desire to see the 'rotten lands' made arable did not stem from the selfish motive of merely wanting to see his property improved. It weighed heavily

upon him that England at that time was experiencing a dire
shortage of corn, an outcome of being incessantly at war with
France and of the whole Continent of Europe being in turmoil as
a result of the activities of Napoleon and his armies. To grow
more grain at home was essential and here at his very doorstep
were hundreds of square miles that could be reclaimed and put
to such use.

By dint of unashamedly harping on the topic he was able at
length to infect his slow-moving neighbours with a measure of his
determination to get something done to this effect. A meeting was
held at Horncastle on 27th August 1799 and a resolution passed
authorizing the employment of John Rennie to do a survey and
report on a drainage system for the area.

With his usual thoroughness and his innate desire always to
look at a problem from its broadest aspects, Rennie made not just
one survey but two—the first in October 1799 and the other in
March 1800, so that he could observe the condition of the land
both before and after the winter rains. In Smiles's words:

> The manner in which Mr Rennie proceeded to work out the
> problem presented to him was characteristic of the man. Most
> of the drainage attempted before his time was of very partial
> and inefficient character. It was enough if the drainers got rid
> of the surplus water anyhow, either by turning it into the
> nearest river, or sending it upon a neighbour. What was done in
> one season was very often undone, or undid itself, in the next.
> The ordinary drainer did not care to look beyond the land
> immediately under his own eyes. Mr Rennie's practice, on the
> contrary, was founded on a large and comprehensive view of
> the whole subject. He was not bounded by the range of his
> physical vision, but took into account the whole contour of the
> country; the rainfall of the districts through which his drains
> were to run, as well as of the central counties of England, whose
> waters flowed down upon the Fens.

Rennie observed that the root of the whole problem was that
during winter the rivers were full of sand and silt in suspension.
With the coming of dry weather this was precipitated to form
sandbanks which impeded the natural flow of rivers and drains to
the sea. The water backed up and burst the defensive banks along
the rivers.

To Rennie the cutting of the deepest possible outlets to the sea
was as obvious as the fact that 'any boy playing at dirt pies in a
gutter knows that if you make an opening sufficiently low to let

the whole contained water escape, it will flow away'. Proper 'out-falls' to the sea much more comprehensive than those there at the time would, he explained, benefit the entire area and be much more efficient that piecemeal attempts at removing the water from particular parts. As simple as this sounds, his scheme met with stubborn resistance from individual landowners who thought merely in terms of the problems of their immediate neighbour-hood and could not bring themselves to embrace a plan which would run to something like £500,000 to put an end to the difficulties of the whole watery region. Years went by in argument before Rennie, staunchly supported by Sir Joseph Banks, was em-powered to carry his scheme into execution.

Those who had been in opposition to Rennie were in due course to do a right-about-face when the benefits started to accrue in the form of vastly increased revenue from their land. In the February 1807 issue of the *Farmer's Magazine*, for ex-ample, there appeared a letter from one Lincolnshire landowner extolling the fact that 'our fine drainage works begin now to show themselves and in the end will do great credit to Mr Rennie, the engineer, as being the most complete drainage that ever was made in Lincolnshire and perhaps in England'.

The gratitude of the smallholder was heartfelt, for no longer were conditions such that horses would subside up to their bellies in the soft, sodden soil if they stood still for any length of time in one place, nor would flat boards have to be nailed to their hooves to enable them to move about at all, and fruit farmers, gathering their crops, would no longer have to go from tree to tree by boat.

6 *The Bell Rock Controversy*

AMONG engineers and between the families of the protagonists a controversy has been going on for more than one hundred and fifty years as to whether John Rennie or Robert Stevenson should be given credit for the Bell Rock Lighthouse.

If the lighthouse were merely a good piece of construction in its field the argument could be dismissed as petty, but not without sound reason has the Bell Rock light been called 'an engineering miracle'.

Completed in 1810 it is the oldest sea-swept lighthouse in the world, and its setting is dramatic. If one stands on the cliffs at Arbroath, near the mouth of the Tay on the east coast of Scotland, one can discern twelve miles out from shore the two-hundred-feet tall lighthouse seemingly rising up out of the sea. One asks oneself first why a lighthouse was built out there in what appears to be the open sea, and then, more baffling, *how* was it built?

The why of Bell Rock lighthouse goes back for centuries. What appeared to be plain sailing for ships coming in from the North Sea to ports on the Forth and the Tay and other ports farther north was not indeed so, because of the existence of what was originally called the Inchcape Rock. It is a stretch of sandstone some two thousand feet long lying off the mouth of the Tay. It is submerged to a depth of about sixteen feet at high tide and at low tide leaves exposed a hundred yards of its high point.

Just what a menace it was to shipping has been immortalized by Richard Southey, Poet Laureate at the time of Rennie, in a ballad which contained the verses:

> They hear no sound, the swell is strong;
> Though the wind hath fallen they drift along,
> Till the vessel strikes with a shivering shock—
> 'O Christ! it is the Inchcape Rock!'

Bell Rock—general view

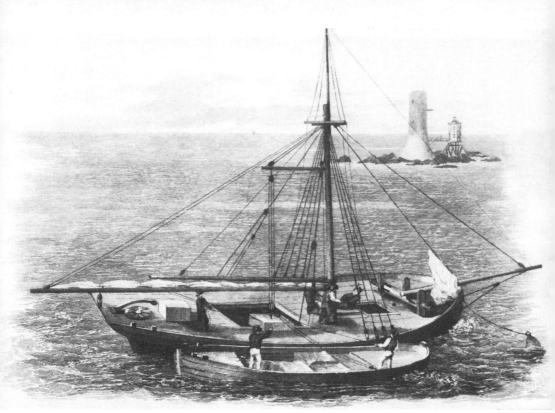

Bird's-eye view of the Smeaton *and praam boat*

View of the Rock and foundation pit

In the fourteenth century the Abbots of Aberbroathock, the old name for Arbroath, went out one day at low tide and managed to affix to the exposed rock a warning bell, adjusted to be kept ringing by the motion of the sea, and it was this that brought the new name of Bell Rock. Not entirely effective, especially on calm days when there were no waves to set the bell clanging, it became completely ineffective as a warning to shipping when a gentleman known in those parts as Sir Ralph the Rover stole it from its moorings for reasons history does not state. However, a year after this ghoulish bit of souvenir hunting irony stepped in and Ralph the Rover was among those to be shipwrecked and perish on the rock in the winter storms.

Time went by, with the rock every year taking its toll, until in 1793 Sir Alexander Cochrane, Commander-in-Chief of the Leith Naval Station on the Firth of Forth, wrote to the Trustees for the Northern Lights proposing the erection of a lighthouse. Much thought was given to the matter but it was eventually decided that such an undertaking was impractical.

In 1799, however, that coast was hit by the worst storm ever recorded. It raged 'for three days with little intermission' and one can get an idea of the ferocity of that December gale from the fact that one ship, on its way to Newcastle from the south, eventually got there but only after taking what was very definitely the long way round. Robert Stevenson wrote of the storm:

A coal ship in ballast returning from London to Newcastle was carried completely round the coast of Great Britain and Ireland, the first land made, after being off Flamborough Head, Yorkshire, being the Land's End of Cornwall. After being refitted it sailed up the Channel, through the Straits of Dover and thence to Newcastle. . . . All other vessels navigating the German Ocean [old name for the North Sea] were drifted upon the Coast of Scotland. Many found shelter in Leigh and Cromarty Roads, but seventy sail of ships were lost when many of their crews perished.

The Inchcape reef claimed the majority of these, including H.M.S. *York*, a warship of seventy-four guns.

This disaster prompted Captain Joseph Brodie, RN, and Joseph Couper, an ironfounder of Leith, to work out a scheme for the erection of a series of beacons on the reef, the expense to be borne by a toll on shipping. They did in fact build the beacons but these did not survive the first winter's storms.

Stevenson was at this time Engineer to the Commissioners of Northern Lights and they asked him to make a report with a view to building a lighthouse on Bell Rock.

Robert Stevenson (not to be confused with Robert Stephenson who helped his father George Stephenson to pioneer the railway era) was born in Glasgow in 1772. His father died when he was two. His mother was in straitened circumstances and he had to start his schooling in a charity school. But then events took a happier turn. His mother married Thomas Smith, who in 1786 became the first Engineer to the newly constituted Northern Lights Commission, and this set the pattern for young Stevenson's life. Instead of entering the church as had been intended he was sent by his stepfather to the Andersonian Institute in Glasgow to study civil engineering and then to the University of Edinburgh. Thomas Smith entrusted him, when still in his teens, with work in connection with lighthouse buildings and the new 'macadam' surfaced roads leading to hitherto inaccessible lights.

It was through his experience in this latter field that later in his life he was commissioned to design the eastern road approaches to Edinburgh, a commission he carried out so efficiently that a well-known architect of the day was to write of them: 'The effect was like drawing up the curtain of a theatre.'

Having been taken into partnership by his stepfather, Stevenson inherited his job with the lighthouse commission in 1796. He held the post for forty-seven years, when it was taken over by his eldest son, Alan, so what with Thomas Smith, Stevenson and his son, the job of Engineer to the Northern Lights was a family affair for the best part of a century.

Stevenson was to build twenty-three lighthouses around the coasts of Scotland and as well as his road-building at Edinburgh he built numerous bridges, gave George Stephenson some valuable ideas about the use of malleable iron for rails on railways, evolved revolutionary light warning systems for lighthouses that are still in use and, to top off his versatility, was prominent in the field of oceanic observations, being the first to discover that the salt waters of the sea flow up the beds of rivers in a stream quite distinct from the outward-flowing fresh water.

He married a daughter of his stepfather by a former marriage and had four sons, all of whom made their mark in civil engineering. His eldest son Alan was as ardent a supporter of him in what was to become known as the Bell Rock controversy as Sir John Rennie was of *his* father. Stevenson's youngest, Thomas, had a son whom he christened Robert Louis and who was to make a literary break-away from the Stevenson engineering tradition. Robert Louis Stevenson also entered into the controversy but although his contribution was far better written than any of the others it suffered somewhat from his lack of engineering knowledge.

In 1800 when the Commissioners of Northern Lights asked Robert Stevenson to report on the idea of a permanent lighthouse for Bell Rock he submitted two designs, one for a cast iron structure with an estimate of £15,012 12s. 8d. and the other for a stone tower, estimated to cost £42,636 8s. 2d. In passing, there are two interesting things to note about this. One was the day on which he delivered the plans—23rd December. It might be felt that two days before Christmas would not be a good time to submit plans for an important project, considering people's preoccupation with yuletide activities, but it should be remembered that even more so then than now, Christmas did not loom very large with the Scots, New Year's Eve being much more important to them. And the other thing is: how could engineers work out to the last shilling and penny the estimated cost of such a project? The answer to this is that the various costs itemized—the numerous materials to be used, labour, etc.—were invariably submitted in round figures and then at the end came an item to cover exigencies, which was always a percentage of the whole and sometimes worked out to odd shillings and pence.

Despite public scepticism about the whole idea the Board of Commissioners of the Northern Lights decided on the tower, a model of which Stevenson had submitted with his plans. They applied to Parliament for an Act which would enable them to raise the money for the project, their scheme being to borrow £30,000 and impose a toll of 1½d. per ton on British and 3d. per ton on foreign shipping that plied north-eastern waters and crossed the latitude of Bell Rock. There was much debate in Parliament as to whether this was the best way to finance it, feeling in some quarters being that a better system would be to place a levy on the ports in the region, which had been the way Smeaton's Eddystone lighthouse near Plymouth had been financed in 1759.

Longer arguments took place in the Commons with regard to the technical details of the structure, so that it was not until 1803 that the Bill went to the House of Lords for its final reading. The Lords threw it out.

It was then that John Rennie came into the picture. The Bill had not been passed because it was felt that the project would have a better chance of success if a leading engineer of the day were called in, and the man they turned to was Rennie.

From that time on, from 1803 through to the completion of the lighthouse in 1810, the two engineers were associated on the project, and these seven years form the basis of the contention between engineers who feel that Rennie has been unfairly slighted as regards credit for its great success and those who feel that the Commissioners of Northern Lights were quite correct in placing a bust of Stevenson in the library of the lighthouse with the inscription '. . . to whom is due the honour of conceiving and executing the great work of the Bell Rock Lighthouse'. This explains the ill-feeling between the descendants of each of the men which, at its height, was such that it could be said that Rennies didn't talk to Stevensons.

To put his case forward, Stevenson wrote a book on the subject. Its bulk alone is impressive. A 'coffee-table' book long before they were alluded to as such, it is more than twice as thick as the modern vast art book. Entitled simply *An Account of the Bell Rock Light-house* and published in 1824 by Archibald Constable and Co., Edinburgh, it was twelve years in the writing and production. It had the backing of the Northern Lights Commissioners. At their meeting on 14th July 1812, they voted a sum of up to £400 to defray the cost of publication.

When Rennie heard that Stevenson was at work on the book he said in a letter to a friend:

> I have no wish to prevent his writing a book. If he details the truth fairly and impartially I am satisfied. I do not wish to arrogate to myself any more than is justly my due, and I do not want to degrade him. If he writes what is not true, he will only expose himself. I bethink me of what Job said, 'Oh that mine enemy would write a book.'

Rennie does not feature prominently in the text and what opinion he would have held about the book was not to be known, since he died three years before its publication.

It is a very readable book, intriguing in its detail of the setting up of the project and the construction of the lighthouse, and at times it is vividly exciting. As we shall see, in one passage in particular Stevenson foreshadows the great ability of grandson Robert Louis to tell a story, with the added sense of drama that came from writing about not fiction but real life.

The first step in the rethinking of the Bell Rock light was for Rennie and Stevenson to go to the rock together in 1804, and in company with one of the Commissioners they walked about on the wet precarious stretch of sandstone lapped by the North Sea swell. From this survey Rennie drew up plans and made drawings of a lighthouse to be one hundred feet in height, forty-two feet in diameter at the base and fifteen feet at the top, with a solid base reaching to thirty feet and the remainder of the structure being hollow with six storeys of accommodation, atop which would be the Argand lamps with parabolic reflectors. The estimated cost: £41,843 15s. 9d.

This plan was submitted to a special Parliamentary committee that had been set up. Rennie and Stevenson gave evidence before the committee and eventually a new Act passed through both Houses and received Royal Assent on 31st July 1806.

More than a year was taken up in preparation prior to starting the actual construction—visiting quarries to select stone (Aberdeen granite was the final choice), setting up a headquarters at Arbroath (the nearest practical port to the rock), leasing boats for going back and forth to the project, hiring workmen. Then, in August of 1807, active operations started on the rock.

For his operation at the rock Stevenson needed five boats. The largest of these was the *Smeaton*, named as a gesture to the builder of the Eddystone light. It was a sailing vessel of sufficient size to take the complement of more than thirty men working at the rock to and from the site and, in its hold, transport all the equipment, granite and ironwork needed in construction. It had a rowboat for ferrying men and materials to the rock when moored off from it, since the reef, even at full tide, was too much of a hazard for the *Smeaton* to go alongside.

The second of the larger boats was the *Pharos* 'floating light ship'. It was moored permanently off the rock and had the twin purpose of providing living quarters for the men when the work was at its height and serving as a warning beacon for shipping until such time as the lighthouse was completed. Moored near by, closer in to the site, were two landing 'praams' (Scandinavian ship's boats of the dinghy type) and these, with the rowboat of the *Smeaton*, were the sole means for the men to get on and off the rock from the *Smeaton* and the *Pharos*.

Although the rock was just roughly the size of a soccer pitch when above water, each of its little ridges and inlets was given a name. There was Port Rennie, Port Stevenson, the Abbot's Ledge and Sir Ralph the Rover's Ledge, Neill's Pool and Watt's Reach. Right in the centre, as construction started, was the circular Foundation Pit and from it radiated what were in effect railway tracks along which trucks laden with materials were man-handled from the four wharves on the outer perimeter of the rock.

The fascinating thing about this little colony that Stevenson set up on Bell Rock was that it could only be inhabited for about three hours when the tide was low. When the tide started coming in Stevenson and his workmen had to depart and soon the whole complex was twelve feet under water. As a result work could only go forward in three hour sessions at the morning and evening low tide. And even at that, such a schedule was possible only in the summer months. In the latitudes of that part of Scotland it does not get really dark at night in midsummer, so that low tide coming in the early hours of the morning represented no hind-rance. In winter, of course, the reverse was true and when the hours of daylight were at their shortest the men could work at only one tide per day, abandoning work altogether on the rock when winter was at its most severe and turning to shore jobs in preparation for resumption in early spring.

The men at work on the rock were warned in a rather dramatic way when the time had come for them to stop what they were doing and save themselves from drowning. The rising tide would reach the forge they always kept going for their ironwork and with a great hissing and spluttering extinguish the fire and shroud the whole rock in clouds of steam.

Even though it was practical to work the rock in the middle of the night in high summer, the working conditions were far from amiable. One can imagine what it was like for the workmen getting up to start their morning session. 'At 4 a.m. the bell rang on *Pharos*', Stevenson wrote, 'and the artificers were given a dram and a biscuit. . . .'

To add to their hardship the *Pharos* was a flat-bottomed vessel given to reacting to each and every movement of the sea. On numerous occasions workmen pleaded with Stevenson 'to go ashore, since they could no longer endure the rolling of the light-ship'. At such times it took all his powers of persuasion to keep them at the job.

To their credit, only once was there anything approaching real mutiny. After a storm which had not fully abated when the morn-ing bell went only eight men and the foreman showed up on deck. The little party rowed to the rock, battling with their oars, 'and upon their return from work there were a group of very shame-faced men on the lightship to greet them'. One other work stoppage had nothing to do with the ardours of the job: 'four men refused Sunday work'. That special Scottish feeling about the Sabbath which, even if less stringent, still persists today prompted Stevenson to make some ardent pleading in view of the urgency of the work:

> Surely, if, under any circumstances, it is allowable to go about the ordinary labours of mankind on Sundays, that of the erection of a light-house upon the Bell Rock seems to be one of the most pressing calls which could in any course occur, and carries with it the imperious language of necessity.

One day when Stevenson and his men were at work on the rock a storm blew up unexpectedly. Of the three landing-boats at the site, one had been sent off by the landing-master on an errand to the mother ship *Smeaton*. The storm hit when it was halfway there and after 'pulling for two hours on the oars to cover one mile', they were approaching the *Smeaton* when the sloop was dragged off its moorings. Only with the greatest difficulty could a line be got to the exhausted men in the rowboat, and when at length that had been brought safely on board the *Smeaton* was some distance from its regular mooring place.

Only two men on the rock—Stevenson and the landing-master —knew that the boat which should have returned to help the two praams take the men off as usual after their work session was miles away, out with the *Smeaton*, which was now itself in difficulties in the storm. The other thirty men on the rock, in ignorance of this, were concentrating on their work at the foundation pit.

As the time approached when the incoming tide would force the workmen to call a halt to their activity and be rowed off, it became clear to Stevenson that the *Smeaton*, battling to get into close range of the rock, would never be able to get her boat off to the men in time. In calm weather twenty-four could be accommodated in the two praams, but when it was rough the safety maximum for each boat was eight. The two boats would be able to take off only half of those on the rock. Stevenson describes the scene vividly:

> One can well understand the mental burden this unfortunate circumstance placed upon the only two who knew about it —the writer and the landing-master—as the workmen went on with their work. In this state of suspense, with almost certain destruction at hand, the water began to rise upon those at work on the lower parts of the site. From the run of the sea upon the rock, the forge fire was also sooner extinguished this morning

than usual and the volumes of smoke having ceased objects in every direction became visible from all sides of the rock.

In this perilous predicament, indeed, he found himself placed between hope and despair, but certainly the latter was by much the most predominant feeling in his mind—situate upon a sunken rock in the middle of the ocean, which, in the progress of flood tide, was to be laid under water to the depth of at least twelve feet in the stormy sea.

The men stopped work and went to the part of the rock where their jackets and stockings were stored. And it was then that they saw that instead of three boats there were only two. They at once realized the significance of this. Nobody said anything. They merely looked at Stevenson. 'All this passing in the most perfect silence, the melancholy solemnity of the group made an impression never to be effaced from my mind.'

There was nothing for it now but to try desperately to work out some means of survival. Stevenson decided that he would first get the men to move to the higher parts of the rock not yet under water. Then he would instruct them to strip to the waist, lighten the boats by the removal of everything except essentials, and then a specified number would get into each boat and the remainder would hang by the gunwhales. Stevenson continued:

> Having issued these instructions, one was of course aware that argument might arise as to who should enjoy the relative security of being in one of the boats rather than merely clutching to it. Scuffles might well ensue and it was hard to say, in the ardour of men contending for life, where it might end.
>
> The writer found that his throat became parched and his tongue refused utterance, and learned by experience that saliva is as necessary as the tongue itself for speech. He then turned to one of the pools on the rock and lapped a little water, which produced immediate relief. But what happiness, when, on rising from this unpleasant beverage, some one called out 'A boat! A boat!' and looking around at no great distance, a large boat was seen through the haze making towards the rock. This at once enlivened and rejoiced every heart.

The 'timeous visitor', in Stevenson's words, was Arbroath pilot James Spink, who had come out just by chance with letters for the men. In two trips by each praam the thankful survivors were ferried to the pilot boat and thence to the *Smeaton*.

Stevenson concludes: 'We had left the rock at 9 a.m. and did not reach the *Smeaton* until 12 in the gale, the men drenched as if dragged astern of the boats.'

But the fact that they had survived at all was a matter of both surprise and relief for Captain Pool, master of the *Smeaton*. Fighting a losing battle against the storm, when the time for full tide had come he had virtually given up hope for the men on the rock, despite the fact that he swore that 'both ship and praam would have gone to the d - - - l, rather than the people on the rock should be left to perish'.

The lighthouse having been completed and opened on 17th November 1810, it was some years before the animosity between the Stevenson and Rennie families over the credit for it became a public controversy. It was noted that Robert Stevenson's book *Account of the Bell Rock Light-house* in 1824, besides its scant mention of Rennie, also implied that the author had been responsible for the design. Rennie's son Sir John, in his *Account of the Breakwater in Plymouth* countered this with his statement that the lighthouse on his father's breakwater was 'on the same principle as that adopted by Mr Rennie in the lighthouse designed and built by him on the Bell Rock'. At once Stevenson's sons, especially Alan, pressed their father's claim in *The Civil Engineer and Architect's Journal*, Alan Stevenson also stating in the piece he did on his father for the *Dictionary of National Biography*: 'Rennie was appointed nominally chief or consulting engineer, to whom Stevenson in any case of difficulty could apply. Rennie, who had no experience of lighthouse construction, suggested various alterations of the design, but to none of these Stevenson gave effect.' This does not, however, tally with the many references in letters from Stevenson to Rennie of the following kind: 'From the dimensions given in your letter of the 13th and the Elevation, I have made a section and working drawings for the lower courses. . . .'

The minutes of the meeting of the Commissioners of Northern Lights at which they decided to go ahead with the work seem to be quite definite about the matter:

> Resolved unanimously. 'That the building to be erected for the purpose of a lighthouse on the Bell or Cape Rock shall be of stone, and that the same shall be erected under the directions of John Rennie, Esq., civil engineer, whom they hereby appoint chief engineer for conducting the work.'

The minutes also contain the proposal to the meeting by Rennie 'that Mr Stevenson be appointed assistant engineer, to

execute the works under his superintendence', with suggestions
as to 'the mode of recompensing him for his trouble and the risk
attending the business'.

A point that is not always brought out is that at the time when
the proposal to build a lighthouse there was being discussed in
Parliament, Rennie had entered his forties and Stevenson was a
young man still in his twenties. Stevenson had a certain reputation up in Scotland but it was nothing compared to the stature
of Rennie, who by then had become a national figure.

In letters from Stevenson to Rennie it is obvious who was in
charge of the operation, and also there are insights into the
advantages the younger man felt he might gain by being associated with John Rennie, the eminent engineer:

Island Glass Light House
Harris
4 Septr 1806

John Rennie

London

> ... But, my Dear Sir, there is another point on which I was to
> advise with you, one which deeply engages the future interests
> of my family; and greatly concerns my future prospects in life.
> I mean the salary I should have from the Commission^{rs} in taking
> the active charge of the erection of the Light-house, under your
> directions. I have accordingly advised with my friends at home
> & amongst the rest with Mr Paterson, the result of which was
> that I should request of you to take charge of this important
> matter for me, and they thought as this work in its nature must
> be attended with the greatest personal danger, and as there
> must be many and continual difficulties to struggle with, you
> would likely consider that whatever thought a handsome allow-
> ance for sea-works upon the shore, it ought in this case to be
> more than doubled. ...

Robert Stevenson

> ... In sending these plans I by no means wish it to be under-
> stood to do anything more than merely lay before you a subject
> which has cost me much trouble and consideration without
> supposing myself to have succeeded fully, on the contrary,
> I am confident that your great experience, and extensive
> practice, must render a subject of this kind familiar in your
> mind, and be highly improved in your hands.

> ... I have sent notice to prevent more stones being quarried
> until this matter is arranged to your wish. ... I will also take

the first opportunity to send you a design of one of the Courses dovetailed to the centre stone for your approbation.

... Through your work at Ramsgate Harbour your connections will be much more than formerly and when I get all & Well finished at Bell Rock, perhaps they may be in want of some person in my way conversant in the management of Lights.

In 1892 the argument was still going strong, for in that year Robert Stevenson's famous grandson, Robert Louis Stevenson, weighed in with further observations supporting their side of the story, in *Family of Lighthouse Builders* and even today descendants of the two families need little prompting forcibly to make known their views.

As a newcomer to the controversy, I have done considerable research into the matter and there is now no question in my mind as to where the true credit lies. Undoubtedly the design was by Rennie, benefiting from experience gained by Smeaton in the building of his Eddystone light. Had Rennie's design not been right, results could have been disastrous. As Samuel Smiles pointed out:

> Mr Stevenson was unquestionably entitled to great credit for the able manner in which he performed his duty; but had any failure occurred, in consequence of a defect in the plans, we apprehend that Mr Rennie, and not Mr Stevenson, would have been held responsible.

But as in numerous other fields of endeavour it is not necessarily the man behind the scenes to whom the final credit is given. For example, Field-Marshal Viscount Montgomery was the hero of Alamein—it is acclaimed as his triumph. But he would never have been able to achieve what he did there without the meticulous planning and brilliant organization of his superior, Field-Marshal Alexander. Nevertheless the magnificent job Montgomery did in the field, on the spot, earned him the credit for a famous victory and the important part Alexander played in it gets much less recognition. Likewise, the work of Stevenson in carrying out Rennie's plan was a fantastic achievement, and even though it goes against the grain for anyone writing a life of Rennie not to side with him, there seems no doubt that the structure on Bell Rock should rightfully be called 'Stevenson's lighthouse'.

7 *Rennie the Man*

IT seems inconceivable that Guy de Maupassant could have derived a plot for one of his stories from something which happened in Scotland, but nevertheless an incident connected with Rennie virtually parallels the plot of the story *Boule de Suif*.

To discuss work on the Crinan Canal, Rennie had occasion to visit the Earl of Eglinton at his castle at Ardrossan on the west coast of Scotland some miles up from what is now Prestwick airport. With him was James Hollingworth, his resident engineer at the canal, and they found themselves travelling in the stage-coach in the company of a group of well-to-do 'Paisley boddies'. When still some distance from their destination the coach succumbed to the jolting on the primitive road across the lonely Ayrshire moors. The rear axle broke and Rennie diagnosed a bad weld. A passing shepherd told them that there was a smithy a mile or so up the road and since none of the Paisley gentlemen felt inclined to help, Rennie and Hollingworth and the shepherd set off with the axle assembly.

The blacksmith, however, pronounced it as far too big a job for him to tackle single-handed. It would have to be sent to Ayr. Despite Rennie's pleading on behalf of the Paisley contingent, who would be faced with an uncomfortable night on the moors, the smith was adamant.

'How many sledge hammers have you?' Rennie asked him.

'Two.'

'All right,' said Rennie, taking off his coat and rolling up his sleeves.

The fire was blown up and with Rennie wielding the small striking hammer and the smith and Hollingworth the sledges, it soon became evident to the smith that despite his well-dressed appearance here was a man who knew what he was about when it came to working at the forge. In the words of a writer knowledgeable about such things describing the incident:

Anyone who has ever watched a blacksmith at work will know how the leader, in the universal language of the craft, speaks to his follower with the small hammer. To the uninitiated there is no apparent reason why the striker should start or suddenly stop, change his angle or the force of his blows, but of course the familiar ring of the small hammer on the anvil contains the instructions, and the heavy thud of the sledge is the obedient response.

In short order the axle was repaired and reassembled and as the blacksmith expressed to Rennie his admiration for his unexpected skill with the hammer Rennie responded by 'sending out for some whisky and water—the water for washing their hands'. With the smithy well paid, the axle was carried back and refitted on the coach.

As the journey was resumed, however, there was a noticeable change of mood among the other passengers. The Paisley gentlemen, far from being grateful, pointedly talked only among themselves or looked out of the windows, making it clear that they very much resented the presumption of two working blacksmiths in travelling as 'inside' (first class) passengers.

On arrival at Ardrossan Castle Rennie discussed his business with the Earl and stayed on overnight. Next morning over breakfast they had resumed their talk when a servant came to say that a traveller wished to see the Earl on business for a few minutes. When told that he would have to wait the servant said that the visitor had stressed the urgency of the matter and the Earl consented. The visitor's face dropped when he saw Rennie, for he had been one of the Paisley passengers in the coach.

'I don't know whether you know . . .' said the Earl, starting to introduce them.

'We've met,' smiled Rennie.

His ability to keep the common touch, if not approved of by such as the 'Paisley boddies', was very much appreciated by the men who worked for him. The respected him as an employer who knew his job from the bottom up, and this meant that he attracted the best talent at all levels. In this respect it is interesting that the 'closed shop' was as much in operation then as it is today, as his son John described it:

They were a particular class of skilled workmen embodied into a special Guild or Craft for making machinery, and they would not on any account admit any man to work with them unless he had been apprenticed for the same number of years to a master millwright as themselves, and it must certainly be admitted that they were a very superior body of workmen, not only good workmen, but good engineers competent to direct others and to superintend mechanical work. They were highly paid, receiving 7s. per day besides extra time. If the masters tried to employ anyone who had not served seven years they struck work and would not return until he had been discharged. They had a committee who examined indentures on pay nights. They were powerful because they were in short supply.

Perhaps one reason why Rennie has not been well known to the public is that he was not an eccentric, as were more than a few of the engineers who were his contemporaries. That colourful character Andrew Meikle has been mentioned earlier, but there were also such men as Brindley, Murdock and Telford.

James Brindley, builder of canals, was illiterate and what Samuel Smiles termed 'probably one of the most remarkable instances of self-taught genius to be found in the whole range of biography'. Unable to refer to the experience of others that had been committed to paper and capable himself of writing down little more than figures, he had to carry everything in his head. When confronted with a problem in his work, as so often happened in the building of his masterpiece, the Manchester Ship Canal, he would furnish himself with a goodly supply of water and bread and go to bed, not to emerge until he had arrived at the solution. If it were a particularly thorny problem, this could mean anything up to three days.

William Murdock, besides being an inventor in his own right and the first to make practical use of coal gas as an illuminating agent, worked with James Watt. He had charge on the spot of Watt's work in draining the mines in Cornwall and he became fanatical about steam engines. People in the house where he liver were awakened in the middle of the night by noises in his room and on investigation found him standing on his bed grappling with a bedpost and shouting, 'There she goes, lads, there she goes!'

Sir John Rennie wrote of making an examination of the progress of land drainage work near the mouth of the Nene in Lincolnshire with Thomas Telford, who outlived Rennie senior by a number of years:

It was a very stormy day, accompanied by lightening, thunder, rain, and a strong south-west wind. We got as far as Crab Hole at low water, when the weather beat us completely, and we were obliged to walk over the muddy shore halfway up to our knees, and drenched to the skin. The rain now came down heavier than ever, so that we had no alternative but to retrace our steps back to the dirty old 'public' at the Ferry, called Cross Keys, about 3½ miles distant. We got back, thoroughly soaked, about three in the afternoon. I immediately stripped and went to bed. Old Telford, being a strong hearty man of about seventy, instead of following my example, ordered a large fire to be made in the only sitting-room there was, called for the newspaper, and sat himself down to dry. After two hours' nap I was thoroughly refreshed, and went down to the sitting-room. When I entered there was such a steam that I could hardly see anything; but approaching the fire, found Telford had nearly dried himself, and he abused me thoroughly for being so effeminate as to go to bed.

It has been said of Rennie that much of his achievement has been overlooked because 'he was content to perform a solid honest job of work with a minimum of self-advertisement'. Mentioned earlier were his innovations such as the use of ball-bearings and the centrifugal governor. The dredging machine as we know it today was a Rennie invention. When building the Hull Docks in 1803 it was necessary to clear the shipping basins of mud and silt. Dredging in those days was done with a large spiked 'walking wheel' slung between two barges which churned up the mud and this was then scooped out with a contraption of bucket and spoons. It was clumsy, time-consuming and inefficient. Rennie evolved a system consisting of an endless chain of spiked buckets powered by a steam engine, which is basically the dredging equipment used today in harbours throughout the world.

Rennie in his time was criticized for the costliness of his designs. But he strongly disapproved of the practice of submitting a low quote to secure a contract and then, with the work in hand, confronting the employers with 'unforeseen' additional expense. A close acquaintance said of him: 'What I like about Rennie is his severe truthfulness.'

He never took up shares in speculative companies which employed him. His view was that the engineer was precluded from mixing himself up with their business since if he became involved in their financial side, either openly or on the quiet, he lost most of his moral influence. In a letter written in 1816 he said: 'Engineers should be entirely independent of these connexions— not dabblers in shares—and free alike of contractors and contracts.'

He did not leave a great fortune. The engineer, newly come to prominence in the Industrial Revolution, did not yet seem to be in a commanding position as far as fees were concerned. He signed the contract for the Kennet and Avon canal, to link London and Bristol by river and canal navigation, in 1790 when he was twenty-nine, and for a project so vast that it was not completed until 1810 it seems surprising that his fee was merely £350. His fee when working on reservoirs and pumping stations for the Manchester Waterworks in 1807 worked out at six guineas a day. Although this might not sound very munificent by modern standards a key of how it related to other salaries paid at the time is contained in an exchange he had with a General Brownrigg, head of the Ordnance Department. When Rennie quoted a charge of seven guineas a day in a bill he submitted, the General exploded, 'This will never do! Seven guineas a day! Why, that is equal to the pay of a Field Marshall!' 'I suppose it could be said that I am a Field Marshal in my profession,' Rennie replied. 'If a Field Marshal in your line had been able to do the work, I am sure you would not have sent for me.' 'Then you refuse to make any abatement?' 'Not a penny,' said Rennie and his bill was paid.

Son John wrote a Life of his father but it is unreadable— literally. His handwriting was such that it puts one in mind of the classic story about bad writing which concerns the type-setter who applied for a job with a newspaper. He was told that if he could decipher the editor's handwritten leaders he would be hired on the spot. They gave him one as a trial and when he set it without difficulty he was given the job of setting the editor's outpouring each night. Other printers at the paper could not credit he could do it so easily and one night they decided to play a joke on him. They took some copy paper and with an old pen filled it with meaningless squiggles. This was solemnly handed to the new man as the editor's leader for the following day's edition. He sat down at his machine and with no trouble at all started setting away, to the amazement of the pranksters. Then he stopped, peered closely at a page of the copy and then got up and went to the editor. 'Excuse me, sir', he said. 'I'm setting your leader for tomorrow and there's a word here that stumps me.' The editor looked where he pointed and then turned on him. ' "Constitutional", you dam' fool,' he bellowed, ' "constitutional!" '

The younger Rennie's manuscript of his father's life is in a large, leather-bound ledger in the library of the Institution of Civil Engineers in London, unpublished and for the most part unread. Cyril T. G. Boucher, however, did undertake the nerve-racking task of unravelling it and uncovered this assessment of his father by his son:

>He was naturally of a quick irritable disposition, so that he felt it necessary to keep it under control and schooled himself accordingly, so that strangers who did not know him were universally impressed with his cool, steady and determined behaviour, and when he chose nothing could so far provoke him as to exhibit an appearance of impatience. He was a general favourite, loved and respected by all classes. He was fond of Society and had plenty of anecdotes with a good way of telling them.

>His personal appearance was very dignified and imposing. He was nearly 6 ft. 4 ins. tall, extremely well proportioned and powerfully built, and in his prime could and did walk 50 miles in a day without fatigue and could easily lift 3 cwts. upon his little finger. His head was extremely fine and majestic with a broad oval open countenance, large expressive blue eyes, high developed forehead, prominent nose slightly curved, with proportionate mouth and chin, and splendid luxurious auburn hair. Sir Thomas Lawrence was going to take his portrait (but died before doing so) and said: 'I shall show him as Jupiter for there never was a more magnificent head'. Sir Francis Chantrey, who did a bust, said that Rennie's head was one of the finest he ever saw.

The Chantrey bust is in the National Portrait Gallery. Raeburn painted him in 1811 and this portrait hangs in the Institution of Civil Engineers.

The bulk of the Rennie papers, more than four thousand items in all, had come down to Major Rennie Maudslay, Assistant Keeper of the Privy Purse at Buckingham Palace. They are now in the National Library of Scotland, in Edinburgh, in the care of James Ritchie, head of the manuscripts department. Admirably cata-logued by his assistant, P. M. Cadell, they occupy forty-four large boxes.

One is struck by the beautiful quality of the notepaper, hand-milled of course in the period before the introduction in quantity of machine-made papers early last century. The writing was done with a quill pen, the characteristically ornate use of thicks and thins in evidence only when the writing was by a clerk; otherwise, it was the practical hand-writing of practical men. Each page of a letter has a small semi-circle torn out of it, midway up the right hand side. In those days before envelopes and postage stamps, letters were folded in a way similar to the modern air-letter and secured with a wax seal; tearing them open at the seal always left its mark at the side of the page. Quill pen writing on high quality paper that was not very absorbent meant much use of blotting paper. Indicative of this is that Rennie's notebooks of the late 1700s have alternate sheets of ruled paper and blotting paper. One needed merely to close the notebook to solve the drying problem, which must have been considered quite a brain-wave by the stationery manufacturer who evolved it.

Cost of postage was paid by the recipient, based on the distance the letter had come and on the number of pages. To cut down on the expense to the person receiving the leter correspondents often used to turn the page around when they had come to the bottom and make a second use of it by writing across what had already been penned. Some letter writers pursued thrift even to the extent of using the page for a third time, diagonally across the first two lines of writing. For those of the eighteenth century it may have worked, but to modern eyes it makes illegible chaos.

Rennie's reports on, say, harbour improvements or a proposed new canal are seen to be little masterpieces of detail. As his son John said, 'he never trusted to any assistant, he worked out everything to the minutest detail and put it down in his own hand'. Likewise he did not follow the practice of leading architects or engineers of today of giving to assistants rough sketches of their designs and getting them to make them up into working drawings. The surviving beautifully drawn designs, with superb water colour artwork and elaborate lettering, are Rennie's own work.

It is not usual for an engineer such as Rennie to be of a poetic turn of mind, but among his papers can be found a poem he wrote when he was thirty-six. Undoubtedly he was a minor poet, especially as regards output.

> Poetry at Toyndrum
> Septr. 28 1797
>
> Barren are Caledonia's Hills,
> Unfertile are her Plains,
> Barelegged are her Brawney Nymphs,
> Bare arsed are her Swains—

The dash seems to denote a pause for further inspiration. Apparently none came, for this is all that is extant of Rennie the poet.

His main hobby was collecting old books and one of his few excursions away from work was to wander around the second-hand bookshops. Books were his one indulgence. In 1820 he confessed to yielding to his 'extravagance' when he asked Sir William Jolliffe, of the well known firm of contractors, Jolliffe and Banks, to bring £300 worth of old books for him from Paris. One book in his extensive library had been especially dear to him. In 1942 when his Waterloo Bridge was being demolished it was found among the coins and other objects that had been deposited under the foundation stone in 1811. One of Rennie's most prized possessions which he wanted to leave to posterity, it was the bible Andrew Meikle had given him on his ninth birthday.

In 1788, shortly after he had settled in London, Rennie became engaged and wrote to his brother George back in Scotland:

I have now to inform you that I am about to change my situation in life by marriage. The lady to whom I am in a few weeks to be united is a Miss Dunsford eldest daughter of Richard Dunsford Esquire of Betchworth in the County of Surrey and with the consent of her father and all her relations. Miss D is a lady of such virtues and qualifications as cannot fail to render me happy. The fortune her father gives is £5,000 in the stocks—one half of which be made over now, the other at his death; Besides this she has great expectations from an uncle who has no children, and worth £50,000, this fortune will come to Mrs R her brother and sisters.

When it is convenient we will be extremely happy to have the pleasure of seeing you here—the happy day is not yet fixed —Miss D having been poorly, but will write when it is so.

Boucher, writing of Rennie, was unhappy about this:

He does not appear to have been a greedy man by nature. There are many records of his generosity to those who worked for him. But it must be admitted that there is little to his credit in this letter. It does give an unfortunate impression that he should refer solely to his betrothed's financial riches, with no accompanying evaluation of her personality or mind.

However, in assessing this letter Boucher does not seem to have carried himself back in time to a period much different from ours today as regards the matter of marriage. In those days the dowry was a major consideration and as such was of immediate interest to the family of any man embarking on matrimony.

Having established that the young lady was of 'such virtue and qualifications' that she could not fail to make him happy, it was quite in keeping with that era for the then twenty-seven-year-old Rennie to go on to discuss the financial aspects.

In the event he did not marry Miss D, for unstated reasons. In 1799 he married Martha Ann Mackintosh, nineteen-year-old daughter of one Lachlan Mackintosh, and she came south for the ceremony at Christ Church, Blackfriars Road, Southwark. Little is recorded of Martha Rennie, save that she was a sensible and friendly woman, with few interests beyond the domesticity at Stamford Street, her life being full enough rearing the nine Rennie children, six of whom survived to maturity.

The two eldest—George, who was born in 1791, and John, born in 1794—are of most interest to us here because as we have seen earlier they were to be closely associated with their father's work. William (1796) went into the Navy. Anna (1798) married a distinguished architect, and Jane (1800) a cousin from Phantassie. James (1806) became a lawyer.

The boys, 'having been taught their letters at home', were given a good education at private schools and John, who was to become the writing member of the clan, had an interesting fellow pupil when he was at Dr Greenlaw's school in Isleworth:

> During the time I was there the most remarkable scholar was the celebrated poet, Percy Bysshe Shelley, who was then about twelve or thirteen, and even then at that early age exhibited considerable poetical talent, accompanied by a violent and extremely excitable temper, which manifested itself in all kinds of eccentricities. His figure was of the middle size, although slight, but well made. His head was well proportioned and covered with a profusion of brown locks; his features regular but rather small; his eyes hazel, restless, and brilliant; his complexion was fair and transparent; and his countenance rather effeminate, but exceedingly animated. The least circumstance that thwarted him produced the most violent paroxysms of rage; and when irritated by other boys, which they, knowing his infirmity, frequently did by way of teasing him, he would take up anything or even any little boy near him, to throw at his tormentors. His imagination was always roving upon something romantic and extraordinary, such as spirits, fairies, fighting, volcanoes &c, and he not infrequently astonished his schoolfellows by blowing up the boundary palings of the playground with gunpowder, also the lid of his desk in the middle of schooltime, to the great surprise of Dr Greenlaw himself and the whole school.

When Rennie's wife died in 1806 his sister Henrietta came from Scotland to keep house for them. She was the unhappy, unmarried one and during an earlier stay at Stamford Street, Rennie had written to his brother George about her troubles:

London, April 25th 1794

... In respect to 'Henry' I am really at a loss what to say, for notwithstanding we pay her every attention in our power, still there is something apparently so unhappy about her that she seldom seems happy in her mind, and she is frequently found when by herself in tears. I questioned her some days since to learn what made her so unhappy, and with some difficulty I learnt that she considered herself as a person having no home and she felt so uneasy at the idea of being obliged to go from one friend's house to another that she could not be happy in that situation ...

But taking over the running of the Rennie household in 1806 and having the interest of coping with the young and by all accounts romping children did wonders for her and it was an amicable arrangement all round. Sad to say, however, her health could not stand up to the switch from the good clean air of Scotland to the vapours of London and she had to return north. A letter to her from Rennie's son George gives an interesting insight into the type of home Rennie maintained at Stamford Street:

10 Jan. 1815

My dear Aunt,
Having a little time to spare I think I cannot better employ it than by writing a line or two respecting affairs in this quarter, to which I am sensible you must have a leaning and anxiety. Indeed we have felt your loss extremely and more particularly since the children have been home as they have been running wild for want of a person capable of controlling them than whom no person was more capable than you; for although their father has great command when he pleases yet he sees them so seldom that his authority cannot often be enough applied from his absence throughout the day to have proper effect. Conceive the two girls and boys left to themselves in the Parlour, the room in a perfect mess of rubbish and confusion, things lying here and there, as you well know and all this carried on with that thoughtlessness which is peculiar to our children more than anybody else's in the best of times and what it must be now.

John and I are perpetually lecturing the 2 girls and particularly Jane, who I am sorry to say is just as young as the youngest, as careless as ever, and little improved by her fine school education so far as regards good manners. Ann is certainly more pliable and would turn out well under proper management, as to the 2 boys they are very well and can be ruled (They are expecting a Miss Smith as Governess, she is going to have a task especially as she seems to have a fault— good nature.) I am animated by no ill will towards them, but a desire to see them become a consolation to their father to see them act and think becoming to their age, not great tall useless girls, women in appearance, children in reality. With respect to other affairs I must tell you that the servants have a merry time of it, if hot rolls in the morning and excellent dinners daily of their own choosing can contribute to it. We have now the following number. Moulds and Williams, Mrs King and her sister, Maria and the cook, making 6 servants and a coachman to employ. My father has got home his new chariot—very handsome it is—he has contracted for two good horses for the year and not per day, got new harness and livery, and in short quite brushes up, and yet notwithstanding this expensive establishment there is still something wanting, somebody to regulate internal affairs and to take that interest which no one but yourself is so capable of. To tell truth we have felt your loss extreme and wish you were back. . . .

George Rennie

With young John thinking about what he wanted to do in life, he wrote of his early ambitions, and it is interesting to note that there is nothing new at all about what people regard today as 'the terrible state of the world':

About this period, and ever since the year 1802, there was nothing but war heard or talked of all over the world. The whole country was as it were turned into a camp; every man capable of bearing arms became a volunteer, and at school even we were regularly drilled to the use of arms; and I was so excited by the extraordinary victories of Nelson and the early career of Wellington that I determined to enter the army.

But to this my father was decidedly opposed, as he wished to bring me up in his own profession. I was therefore reluctantly obliged to give up all idea of the military profession and follow that of a civil engineer.

Rennie was a strict father. Letters from eldest son George and second son John frequently started with such things as (from

George) 'I am impressed with sorrow at your displeasure of my conduct & the unfavourable light in which it appears to have been presented. . . I fear you lose patience with me. . . .' (and from John) 'I have never felt the pangs of sorrow & contrition so severely as at the reproofs & reflections contained in your letter. . . .' But it would appear that Rennie was no more severe than was usual in that period when the father was the dominant force and focal point of family life.

George, who had been named after Rennie's admirable oldest brother, was to make a name for himself in his own right as a mechanical engineer and he joined John on his father's death to complete the vast Rennie undertakings and to carry on the machinery business at Holland Street. Undoubtedly more talented than John, it seems certain that it would have been he rather than John who would have been entrusted with the work of carrying through Rennie's plans for London Bridge and other big engineering projects around the country. But George was a cripple.

As we have seen, the two brothers made a great success of the machinery business, including the introduction of such novelties as the first biscuit-making machinery, but they did not necessarily get on well together. George was a strict Presbyterian, as befitted the Rennie Scottish background, and he viewed with disapproval John's changing his denomination to the Church of England on his marriage to the daughter of a peer. George also shared the family feeling about John's knighthood.

When John accepted the knighthood his father had been at pains to reject, members of the Rennie family were disgusted, especially since he became Sir John on the day of the opening of the new London Bridge—the conception of his father. As his aunt, Lorna Macintosh, wrote to a friend: 'Whereas his father was interested in the building of memorable constructions, John it would seem is more interested in proffering the shoulder for accolades.'

The fact that Rennie's working day was from 5 a.m. when he got up until midnight and that he rarely 'took play' placed a serious strain on his health and in his sixtieth year he was under the constant advice of his doctor. In the late summer of 1821 when his son John was in Italy on one of his numerous trips to the Continent he received a message to return to London as quickly as possible. He hastened across France and at Boulogne embarked on a packet boat which took three hours to cross to Dover in a severe gale, and taking the first coach available he got up to London late at night. He wrote:

On arrival I found my father in very bad health, lying upon the sofa in the principal front bedroom; he was glad to see me.

He continued in the same weak state, although in perfect possession of all his great faculties, dictated to me several letters on business, and talked of sundry new works that he was about to undertake, particularly the new London Bridge, and the removal of the old one, which had been for some time under discussion in Parliament; a Bill for this purpose had actually been introduced during the past session, and my father had been requested to prepare a design for it, which he did, and it was very similar to that since executed by myself. My father's bodily health appeared to decline gradually; he was confined almost to the sofa, and could do little more than walk across the room; in this manner he continued until the 3rd October. He went to bed as usual, perfectly sensible and composed, and hoped that he would soon be better, as he was most anxious to return to business and make up for lost time. I went to his room on the morning of 4th of October, and found considerable change for the worse had taken place; he seemed to be in much pain, and was walking about the room, evidently scarcely knowing what he was about. I got him into bed, and immediately sent for his physician, Dr Ainslie who had known him all his life, but was unfortunately out of town. The apothecary, Mr Welbank, came, and we consulted together as to whom we should send for, and ultimately summoned Dr Roberts, who, although in good practice, had never seen my father, and consequently knew nothing of his constitution or complaints. He did the best he could but evidently thought the case was very serious. My father lay in bed all day, almost unconscious, although I thought he knew me. I remained with him nearly the whole day, and about five o'clock in the afternoon he appeared to be sinking fast, and breathed very heavily, which alarmed us all excessively. In a short time this ceased, his features began gradually to relax, and he breathed his last at half-past five on the afternoon of the 4th of October, 1821 in the sixty-first year of his age.

The disease that killed my poor father was that of the kidneys and liver, as far as we could ascertain. All my brothers and sisters were assembled round his deathbed. It was a sad, sad, sight, and afflicted us most severely.

He was universally known and respected; the news of his death spread immediately throughout the town, the public papers were filled with leading articles giving accounts of his public and private life, and everybody deplored the loss.

*Stamford Street
house in 1910*

*National Library
of Scotland,
Edinburgh*

*Garages now where
Rennie's house once stood*

Rennie's Wharf

View of London Bridge in 1616 by J. Visscher

Interior of coffer dam　　　　　　　　　　*British Museum*

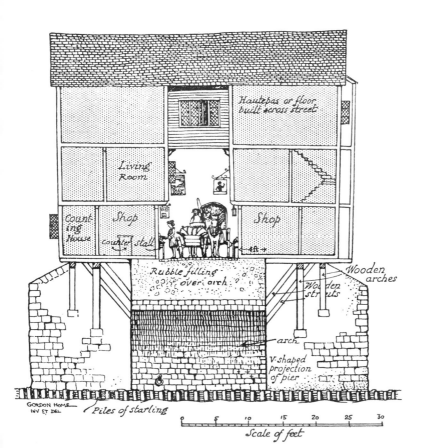

Hautepas or floor built across street

Living Room

Count ing House

Shop

counter stall

Shop

4ft

Rubble filling over arch

Wooden arches

Wooden struts

arch

V-shaped projection of pier

GORDON HOME INV ET DEL

Piles of starling

Sectional drawing of Old London Bridge

British Museum

0　　5　　10　　15　　20　　25　　30

Scale of feet

One of the most powerful and touching articles was written by his talented friend Perry, the proprietor of the *Morning Chronicle*.

It seemed to be the universal wish that he who had rendered so many services to his country and was so generally beloved, should be buried in St Paul's, and arrangements were made accordingly. The funeral took place a few days afterwards, at eleven o'clock, and he was attended to his last resting place by a vast concourse of literary, scientific and private friends.

The epitaph unveiled at the ceremony read:

Here lie the mortal remains of
JOHN RENNIE
F.R.S. F.A.S.
Born at Phantassie in East Lothian
7th July 1761
Deceased in London 4th Octr. 1821
THIS STONE
is dedicated to his private virtue
and records
the affection and the respect of
his family and his friends
but
the many splendid and useful works
by which
under his superintending genius
England, Scotland and Ireland
have been adorned and improved
are
THE TRUE MONUMENTS
OF
HIS PUBLIC MERIT
Waterloo—Southwark—Bridges
Plymouth Breakwater
Sheerness Docks &c. &c. &c.

The epitaph, which owes more than a little to the famous Wren tribute, was composed by John Wilson Croker, First Secretary of the Admiralty at the time and a man with whom Rennie had a close relationship through Admiralty contracts. Croker had a reputation outside his official Government work and worked with Nash as a co-member of the Committee of Taste which was responsible among other things for the conception of Trafalgar Square. Also Croker originated the Athæneum Club in 1824, 'for men distinguished in science, literature and art', and

Sir John Rennie felt privileged to be invited to be a charter member.

There is an error in the lettering of the epitaph. Rennie's date of birth should read '7th June 1761' but since the mistake was not discovered until some time afterwards it was allowed to stand. The stone chosen for his last resting place was appropriately a plain rectangular prism of polished granite of the type which Rennie was among the first to use extensively and which he incorporated into the design of his new London Bridge.

8 'Nell Gwyn Slept Here'

IF one goes today to Stamford Street, S.E.1, which links the
southern approaches to Waterloo Bridge and Blackfriars Bridge
and was the street where Rennie lived, one finds oneself in a
depressing part of London. There are some relatively modern
office buildings but in the main all one sees are seedy terraced
houses standing there with the look of run-down dwellings merely
awaiting demolition. There is building activity in the area, particularly on the nearby riverfront where abandoned wharves are
being dismantled to make room for new development, and one
feels that the time will soon come for the dreary Stamford Street
terraces to go. In the meantime, however, there is no pleasure to
be derived from walking along the forlorn street to seek out what
used to be Rennie's home at No. 52, now the site of garages.
There is a plaque there on the bleak garage wall to inform
passers-by that it was formerly the residence of John Rennie and
the adjoining narrow road that runs down to the river is labelled
Rennie Street. But no admirer of the man's work, viewing the
drab scene, could feel that this was a happy acknowledgement to
him.

In earlier times it had been quite different. The house in which
Rennie and his wife Martha brought up the six of their nine
children who survived was in what son Sir John described in his
autobiography as 'one of the most fashionable suburbs of the
metropolis'. Besides being in those days 'a good address', it was
also very convenient for Rennie, being but a stone's throw from
the site of the Albion Mills he had come to London to build in
the 1780s and in the course of time equally handy to the setting
for his Waterloo Bridge.

Across the river from *The Times* in Printing House Square,
that particular area on the south of the Thames known as
Bankside embraced such well known places as the Globe Theatre,
the Bear Garden, one of the city's leading centres of the lively

sport of bear baiting, the Bishop of Winchester's Palace. Bankside had a very colourful history, enlivened at two different periods by the residence there of two spectacular ladies.

In the early 1600s one of the leading procuresses in London during Charles I's reign gloried in the name of Donna Britannica Hollandia. Having been evicted from her place of business and having only just avoided going to Newgate Prison, she felt she had better move out of town and find a new locale for her activities. Across the river in Southwark she rented an old moated mansion in Paris Garden. At the height of her notoriety a gentleman with the equally splendid name of Shackerley Marmion published 'An Historical Discourse of the Life & Actions of Donna Britannica Hollandia, Arch-Mistress of the Wicked Women of Utopia', which incidentally did so well it was turned into a play. Marmion wrote that her big house was 'a place fit for her purpose, being wondrous commodiously planted for all accommodations'. Also it was close to the Globe and Hope theatres, to which young gallants of the city resorted, so she could be ensured of a good spill-over trade. However, such a popular rendezvous did her house become that Madam Holland, as she was familiarly known, eventually attracted the attention of the local authorities and a group of peace officers were sent to evict her and bring her to court. But she was not the sort to go down without a fight. She organized a strong defence against them and the fact that the moat around the house was always full in that low-lying area adjoining the river helped her immeasurably in turning her brothel into a stronghold. Marmion's discourse was in fact published when the continued efforts of the peace officers to dispossess her were still in progress. Using the old word for a besieged camp, he referred to it as 'Holland's Leaguer' and from then on that was the name by which it was always known, even after the beleaguered Madam Holland had at length been removed and brought to justice.

By the time Charles II came to the throne, in 1660, Holland's Leaguer had been pulled down and on the site was an avenue of attractive houses standing in their own grounds, the name being perpetuated in its title of Holland Street. Some years later, having established his close friend Nell Gwyn in a gracious town house in Pall Mall, Charles II decided that she should have also a country home and in his search for a suitable retreat for her he settled upon one of the houses in Holland Street.

More than a century later, by 1810, Rennie had not only made his name as one of the leading engineers of the day, engaged in building bridges, canals, harbours and other works throughout the United Kingdom but he had also built up an extensive business as a manufacturer of machinery. When the Albion Mills burnt down in 1791, he and others had prepared schemes for rebuilding. Nothing had come of this, so with the land lying idle he had bought it and set up his workshops there. As his business grew he needed more space. The thing to do to provide extra workshops and storerooms would be to buy up some of the old deserted houses adjoining his main works—in Holland Street. One of which, of course, had been Nell Gwyn's.

Despite the fact that when Rennie's workmen moved in more than a hundred years had elapsed since King Charles had sipped tea and enjoyed other diversions with Sweet Nell in her Holland Street country house, it still retained much of its former elegance. The elaborately scrolled ceilings and the richly panelled walls of a bygone era provided an interesting contrast to the stored-up piles of machine parts of the Industrial Revolution at its height.

From 1810 onwards first Rennie and then his surviving sons operated from there a thriving business in engineering machinery, with export orders among its most important aspects, including 'Arms for Russia' which were to feature in the Crimean War of the middle 1850s. Sir John wrote:

When my father died he left this machinery department to my brother George and myself. We continued the business, rebuilt the place entirely, with considerable improvements, and did a large amount of business here. We constructed the rolling mills for the Calcutta and Bombay mints; numerous locomotive engines for different railways, amongst others the 'Satellite' for the Brighton Railway, which was one of the first that attained the speed of 60 miles an hour upon the gauge. [Average speed on London to Brighton route today: fifty-nine miles per hour.] We made the steam engines and machinery for Her Majesty's ship 'Bulldog', the yacht 'Dwarf', and others; also for the famous Russian Steam 'Vladimir', which did so much mischief at Sebastopol; two yachts for the Emperor of Russia and other vessels for the Russian navy, together with the whole of the iron gates for the dockyard at Sebastopol, two pair of which were brought back as trophies by the British and French armies. We made and erected the small arms manufactory at Constantinople, for making five hundred muskets per week. We constructed the engines and machinery for the 'Archimedes' screw-vessel, which was the first screw used in this country; and again, the iron vessel, engines and screw for the 'Dwarf' which was the first screw-vessel ever introduced into the British Navy, in the year 1839. We built four iron steam vessels and their machinery for the Russian Government, for the Caspian Sea, which were the first that floated on its waters; they were first built in London, then taken to pieces, sent to St Petersburg, and thence down the Volga to the Caspian; men were sent with them by us, who put them together there, and launched them successfully.

To complete the saga of the engineering works established by Rennie, it should be mentioned that sons John and George found it necessary to build new and larger workshops at Woolwich, which was not surprising at the rate they were going. Most of their buildings in Bankside were pulled down to make way for the railway to the new Blackfriars Station in the 1870s. When George Rennie, who was in fact the leading light in the concern despite brother John's exuberance, retired the Rennie business at Woolwich passed into other hands, eventually fell into decline and was finally wound up in 1885.

To go today to the site of Rennie's engineering business one can walk, as he used to do each day, from what was his house in Stamford Street across the southern approach road to Blackfriars Bridge and there by the river is a building boldly labelled Rennie's Wharf. But of the workshops of which this was an adjunct there is now no trace to be seen. The railway into Blackfriars Station across the river was built right over them, elevated on tall Victorian stone arches. Underneath the arches was what for some time was the Blackfriars Goods Station but is now a place of eerie semi-darkness used by commuters into London as a car park.

In trying to find the site of Nell Gwyn's house in what are now the drab buildings of the area, one is confused by the fact that Holland Street is nowhere to be found—until someone is good enough to tell you that the name has been changed to Hopton Street, the street on which Rennie's Wharf stands. Local people are hazy as to where precisely Nell Gwyn lived, and even a chat with the borough archivist is no more helpful. However, adjoining Rennie's Wharf is a building, put up in 1907, which bears a plaque with the information: 'The house formerly on this site was frequented by Sir Christopher Wren.'

Now, not very far along the river there is another plaque which says that Wren lived there during the building of St Paul's, the front windows affording a fine view of the cathedral across the Thames, an ideal spot for him to watch it taking shape. It makes an interesting piece of conjecture that the house on old Holland Street that he 'frequented' was in fact Nell Gwyn's country home and that King Charles, making the journey there to visit her, would kill two birds with one stone and get Wren to join them so that he could discuss progress at St Paul's.

In 1910 the local borough council decided that Stamford Street should be renamed Rennie Street and this was greeted with approval from the *Daily Graphic* in a story under the headline 'RENNIE STREET, SOUTHWARK—Belated Honour to the Builder of Waterloo Bridge':

> After allowing one of the greatest bridge engineers of all times to lie unhonoured and unsung for the better part of a century —we did bury him in St Paul's to be sure—we are now taking the liberty of using his name for the purpose of rechristening Stamford Street, a poor thoroughfare on the south side of the river between Waterloo Bridge and Blackfriars. . . . Few will be sorry to know that the name of Stamford is to be changed to Rennie, for the sake of this poor street, once beautiful, no doubt, and useful. . . .

Other papers enlarged on the subject of what a mean street it had become, including one report which stated:

> Stamford Street has had a mixed life. Sixty to seventy years ago there were many well-to-do houses there but by 1890 it became notorious as the home of some of the worst characters in London. In one house alone there were three tragedies in the space of two years. Dr Neill Cream, the prisoner, murdered two small girls. A young gardener threw himself from a third-floor window and impaled himself on the area railings. And a woman was convicted for a particularly bad case of kid-napping, the details being of the most disgusting character. For years it has been the lowest 'Bohemia' in London. In its favour, however, it must not be forgotten that the famous Stamford Street Unitarian Chapel and the Hospital for Diseases of the Skin, still carry on their good work there.

This prompted much discussion as to what a doubtful privilege it was to have one's name associated with such a sordid thorough-fare and in the end it was decided that Rennie should be honoured at a neighbouring street, smaller but not of such ill repute.

9 Harbours and Docks

OF the more than four hundred projects Rennie undertook during his working life, from the designing of his first mill in 1779 to his plans for London Bridge in the year of his death in 1821, about a quarter of his work was connected with harbours and docks. Just as one cannot travel far in the British Isles without encountering a Rennie bridge or canal, there are few harbours in the country for which he was not asked to furnish reports for the authorities and in a great number of cases proceeded with the building of new or the extending and rehabilitating of existing harbours and docks. If one makes a voyage right around the coast from Aberdeen to Glasgow, stopping off on the way at Hull, Yarmouth, London, Dover, Portsmouth, Plymouth, Newquay, Liverpool, Dublin and Belfast, one will have called in at just a small percentage of the harbours on which Rennie worked.

The first time he was called upon to report on harbour facilities was in 1793 when the Commissioners of British Fisheries asked him what could be done about improving the harbour of Wick, the only haven capable of affording shelter for ships in the worst of weather which was to be found in a stretch of a hundred and twenty miles of rock-bound coast in South Wales. His bold plan which called for the scrapping of the existing jetties and the building of an entirely new harbour with canal and basin to accommodate the trade of Wick was considered altogether too drastic and was not put into effect. At a later date when changes *were* made at Wick the authorities were to regret not going ahead with his scheme, since 'the plan since adopted, though exceedingly costly, does not seem calculated to secure the objects which would have been obtained by executing Mr Rennie's more comprehensive yet much more economical design'.

Rennie's thoroughness and his faculty for rethinking a whole situation in its broadest terms rather than merely making piecemeal changes to what already existed caused other port authorities who commissioned reports from him to be as hesitant as those in charge at Wick and it was not until 1797 that he became engaged in actual harbour work. At Grimsby in that year he furnished a plan of the great lock which it was necessary to place at the entrance of the canal leading to the dock and was in his opinion indispensable for solving the problem of keeping the harbour entrance clear of silt.

When the construction of the lock was in progress a portion of the retaining walls gave way. On investigation it was found that the defect lay in the nature of the ground on which the foundation was built. It was too soft to bear the weight of ordinary solid walls. To overcome this, Rennie decided that without diminishing the quantity of material used it should be distributed over a broader base, thus providing a larger load-bearing surface. Following this reasoning the quay walls were built with hollow centres, a revolutionary form of construction. The practice was to be widely adopted by engineers confronted with similar circumstances and was regarded as such a valuable innovation that some years after Rennie had pioneered the idea Sir Samuel Bentham, in 1811, took out a patent for it in his name—'of which', Samuel Smiles commented, 'Mr Rennie took no notice'.

In England in 1803 there was an invasion scare not dissimilar to that which was to grip the country more than a century later, although on this occasion it was not German landing craft gathering at ports across the Channel but 'Napoleon's legions assembled on the heights above Boulogne and his flat-bottomed boats crowding its port'. Belgian newspapers were openly speculating how long it would take the French army to reach London. The British military authorities hastened to examine schemes for defences on the eastern approaches to the city, where it was felt most likely that there would be an advance of enemy forces landing near the mouth of the Thames or on the Essex coast, and Rennie was consulted with a view to his devising a plan for checking the approach of the French from that quarter. After studying the terrain he laid before the Government a plan whereby the Lea Valley could be flooded at will by means of a series of dams with sluices at the junction with the Thames (adjoining what was to become the East India Docks) and at other points further up the Lea.

At this time Rennie was consulted also about improvement of the defences of Kent and he laid out a plan which he designated the Hythe Military Canal, to extend westward some twenty miles

from Hythe to Rye, with earthworks on the inland side to further
deter possible invaders who had already been exposed to fire when
overcoming the hazard of the canal. At this part of the coast a
harbour was needed to accommodate frigates engaged in watching
the opposite shore. Rennie was in favour of Folkestone as the
best site and submitted a design to turn what was then a small
basin into a haven for the naval craft.

Not all these projects were completed. The Hythe Military
Canal was built, some of the work on the dams for flooding the
Lea Valley was done, but there was nothing built at Folkestone,
for the invasion scare subsided when Napoleon, precisely as
Hitler was to do, 'diverted his warlike ambition elsewhere'.

In the course of his work on Britain's defences Rennie made the
acquaintance of Pennsylvania born Robert Fulton (1765–1815),
credited as 'inventor of the steamboat' in America but not elsewhere, since his steamboat patents were merely improvements to
basic developments patented by others in Europe. Fulton, who
spent a good deal of his time in Europe, had switched the offer of
his inventive sub-genius from France to Britain and Rennie was
member of a commission appointed by the British Goverment to
investigate Fulton's invention of 'a torpedo for the blowing up of
ships at sea'. To let him demonstrate the powers of his 'infernal
machine' an old hulk standing in Walmer Roads, Kent, was
placed at his disposal. In the words of a contemporary report: 'He
succeeded, after an unresisted attack of two days, in blowing up
the wretched carcass, and with it his pretensions as an inventor.'

Rennie had no hesitation in branding Fulton as a quack who
traded on the inventions of others. He wrote:

> I consider that little merit belongs to him in regard to the
> invention of the steamboat. Jonathan Hulls, Miller of Dalswin-
> ton, and Symington had been at work upon the invention long
> before Fulton; Miller having actually made a voyage to Sweden
> and back with his steamboat as early as 1789, eighteen years
> before Fulton made his first successful experiment on the
> Hudson.

In a letter sent to a friend in the Admiralty with a copy of
Fulton's book in which the author implied he was the inventor of
cast iron bridges, Rennie wrote:

> The merit he has—if merit it may be called—is a proposal for
> extending the principle previously applied in this country. The
> first iron bridge was erected at Coalbrookdale in 1779, and

between that and the publication of Fulton's book in 1796 many others were erected; so that, in this department, he has little to boast of. I consider Fulton, with whom I am personally acquainted, a man of slender abilities, though possessing much self-confidence and consummate impudence.

Rennie's Plymouth Breakwater is one of the most highly regarded of all his major works. The problem at Plymouth was that although its three-miles-wide Sound afforded an abundance of deep water and its location at the entrance to the English Channel made it ideal as a naval station, gales beating in from the south-west did not make it a secure anchorage. At the beginning of the 1800s the Admiralty examined various plans put forward, most of them based on the idea of building a pier out from either one side of the entrance to the Sound or the other. When Rennie was asked to do a study of the situation he pronounced all these unsatis-factory, since in time such piers would induce silting up of the inner reaches of the Sound. On 22nd April 1806, he submitted his own £1,102,440 scheme to build a mile-long breakwater in the middle. This was dismissed by many as visionary and im-practicable. Others held that it would destroy the Sound for purposes of navigation and lead to its complete silting up. Argument was to go on for five years but at length the Lords of the Admiralty were fully convinced of the merits of Rennie's plan and the powers to implement it were granted by an Order in Council issued on 22nd June 1811.

A piece of land was bought from the Duke of Bedford at Oreston, up the Catwater at the head of the Sound, this ground containing twenty-five acres of limestone, considered ideal for the work. A quarry was opened, wharves and cranes built, and a railway laid down to carry the stone to the specially constructed boats that would take the stone five miles down the Sound and dump it into the water. On 12th August 1811, the Prince Regent's birthday, the first load was deposited and for nearly two years the barges went back and forth dumping the rubble at the line of buoys marking the site without any visible sign of the breakwater taking shape, but then in March 1813 parts started to be visible at low water. By March of the following year a continuous line of more than seven hundred yards was above water and ships caught in storms in the Channel were beginning to take advantage of its tranquillizing effect on the waters of the Sound. In 1815 when Napoleon entered Plymouth Sound on board the *Bellero-phon* he expressed his admiration of the work. Rennie was much gratified when the ex-Emperor's comments were relayed to him.

On 12th August 1815, four years from the start, the records showed that no less than 615,057 tons of stone had been deposited and the length above low water was 1,100 yards. In the following year, with the rubble being dumped at the astonishing average daily rate of 1,030 tons of manhandled blocks of from two to twelve tons each, the one-million mark was passed and in January 1817 the soundness of Rennie's plan was proved when the unfinished work survived a series of violent storms. His building technique was the same as he had employed when constructing the harbours at Howth and Kingstown, in Ireland, and at Holyhead—throwing in blocks to a given line and allowing the motion of the sea to form the slope at which they would settle, thus saving expenditure of much time and labour. 'To gain the proper slope', he said, 'it is best to follow the laws of nature—the waves are the best workmen.'

At the time of his death in 1821 a total of 2,381,521 tons had been dumped and the breakwater, then 1,200 feet short of its planned 5,100 feet, withstood in 1824 another onslaught of gales even more fierce than those of 1817. In 1848, when the work may be said to have been completed, the total quantity of stone deposited was 3,670,444 tons, plus 22,149 cubic yards of masonry facing the exposed upper part of the breakwater. Still to be seen there well over a century later, it consists of an amount of material equal to that contained in the Great Pyramid.

Rennie was to do much other work for the Admiralty, including royal dockyards at Sheerness at the mouth of the Thames and at Portsmouth. In the latter case it was a matter of radical rebuilding, Rennie stating in his report:

> Let any stranger visit Portsmouth Dockyard, the head establishment of the British navy, he will be astonished at the vastness and number of buildings, and perhaps say, 'What a wonderful place it is!' knowing nothing about the subject. But I can compare the place to nothing else than a pack of cards, with the names of different buildings, docks, &c, marked upon them, and then tossed up into the air, so that each in falling might find its place by chance—so completely are they devoid of all arrangement and order.

But outside this Admiralty work, his most notable civil engineering in connection with harbours was undoubtedly his building of London Docks.

In order to avoid confusion when writing about London's dockland one should at the outset draw attention to the difference between the London docks and London Docks. The former ('docks' with a small 'd') refers to the whole accommodation for ships coming into the port; the latter, like the West India and East India Docks and so on, is merely one of those which made up the whole. Starting in 1798, Rennie built the London Docks, forerunner and model for those which were to be built in the following century and after at the Port of London.

An interesting point is that Rennie was called in to undertake this work not because London was so much in need of better facilities for handling the greatly increased shipping making use of the port. The authorities sought his help primarily to combat the much bigger problem—the pilfering and smuggling that had assumed such proportions that it had become one of the main activities of those who worked on the river.

It is true, though, that the accommodation in the Pool of London was quite inadequate for coping with the big increase in trade. From 1750 to the closing years of the eighteenth century the number of vessels coming into London annually had trebled to 13,500 (today 54,000). Without adequate quays for them, most of the colliers and coasters, the ships from Continental ports and those engaged in the booming East India and West Indian trade had to anchor in midstream and have their cargoes taken by lighter up the river to the warehouses. The congestion of ships, lighters, barges, watermen's boats and other assorted craft made conditions on the Thames chaotic.

But the most disturbing aspect, as far as the Government was concerned, was what was happening to the unloaded cargoes. Samuel Smiles wrote:

The warehouse accommodation was found very inadequate in extent as well as difficult of access. There was a regular system of plunder carried on in the conveyance of the merchandise from the ship's side to the warehouses. Lightermen, watermen, labourers, sailors, mates and captains occasionally, and even the officers of the revenue, were leagued together in a system of pilfering valuables from the open barges. The lightermen claimed as their right the perquisites of 'wastage' and 'leakage' and they took care that these two items should include as much as possible. There were regular establishments on shore for receiving and disposing of the stolen merchandise. The Thames Police was established, in 1798, for the purpose of checking this system of wholesale depredation; but so long as the goods were conveyed from the ship's side in open lighters, and the open quays formed the principal shore accommodation—sugar hogsheads, barrels, tubs, baskets, boxes, bales and other packages being piled up in confusion on every available foot of space —it was clear that mere police regulations would be unequal to meet the difficulty.

Mr Colquhoun, the excellent Police Magistrate, estimated that in 1798 the depredations on the foreign and coastal trade amounted to the almost incredible sum of £506,000, and on the West India trade to £272,000—together £738,000! He stated the number of depredators—including mates, inferior officers, crews, revenue officers, watermen, lightermen, watchmen &c —to be 10,850; and the number of opulent and inferior receivers, dealers in old iron, small chandlers, publicans &c, interested in the plunder, to be 550. Colquhoun's book, *Commerce and Police of the Thames*, and its description of the lumpers, scuffle-hunters, long-apron men, bumboat men and women, river-pirates, light-horsemen and other characters who worked at the water-side, with their skilful appendages of jiggers, bladders with nozzles, pouches, bags, sacks, pockets &c, form a picture of life of the Thames to rank with Mayhew's *London Labour and London Poor*.

As well as what appears to have been highly organized pilfering the confused way in which imports were brought ashore made it ideal for smuggling, which was on such a scale that honest merchants complained bitterly about how their prices were constantly being undercut by goods that had clearly come into the country illegally.

The Government had long been badgered by traders demanding security for their shipments and now that they were made aware of the extent of the Customs revenue they were losing to the smugglers they decided to remedy these evils.

In June 1798 Rennie was consulted and asked to devise a plan. He ruled out the suggestion that quays and warehouses should be built on both sides of the river. He felt that the tideway should be relieved of much of its clutter of ships. Land abutting the Thames should be appropriated for the building of docks and basins communicating with the river. Everything—the docks, vessels, quays, warehouses etc.—could be locked behind high enclosing walls, safe from the plunderers. Not entirely revolutionary, since some docks already existed at British ports, it was much broader in scope than anything which had previously been envisaged and much more costly, since a vast number of houses and other buildings would have to be acquired and demolished even before work could be started on the ambiguously named 'floating docks' (it is not the docks themselves but the vessels in them that float).

Nevertheless his scheme was adopted and the purchase and clearing of the site about half a mile downstream from the Tower of London took just short of three years. In the spring of 1801 work on the actual docks commenced with the erection of two steam engines of 50 h.p. each for pumping water, pile-driving, grinding mortar and sundry other purposes, which was described as 'an application of steam power as an economist of labour of which Mr Rennie was a pioneer in the execution of such works'. His over-all plans for the docks encompassed the use of steam to work the cranes at the finished docks but this, among other innovations he suggested such as the building of a tramway for trucks right around the docks to cut down time-wasting man-handling of cargoes, was not carried through. Although on his own building projects Rennie could use newly developed labour-saving devices such as steam power, this was not to mean that those hired to work in his finished product would take kindly to such new-fangled ideas. The day-to-day workers who were to be employed at his completed London Docks let it be known that they would not stand for the introduction of steam power; the cranes, as always, must be worked by hand. The same sort of resistance is still put up by the working man today, in opposition to container cargoes in those same docks in London.

Rennie's London Docks were opened 'with considerable cere-mony' on 30th January 1805, but even before they were completed he had been commissioned to build another set of docks farther down the river. Financiers foresaw the great commercial value of floating docks and in 1803 a group of them formed a company to provide accommodation on the Thames exclusively for the use of the vessels of the East India Company. The necessary Act of Parliament was obtained, a site was purchased at the Blackwall bend of the river and what were to become familiar as the East India Docks were finished and opened for business on 4th August 1806.

As we shall see, just as Rennie's Thames bridges, built for the horse and buggy days, have had to yield to the demands of modern motorized transport in the metropolis, so too his docks in London's port, built for the sailing-ship days, are now not capable of coping with modern shipping. It is not merely a matter of size, not merely the fact that they are docks designed to take ships of up to 4,000 tons in an age of 250,000-ton tankers; smaller ships still exist and must be catered for. What sealed their doom was the revolution in cargo handling. In Rennie's day and indeed up to a decade or so ago all cargo was loaded and unloaded piece by piece. Now we are in the era of container freight and other 'unit' cargoes such as timber, paper and pulp which combine into much larger units which can be handled much more easily and more speedily—if you have the dock space and equipment to do it. To enlarge and re-equip London's up-river docks such as Rennie's London Docks, West India, East India, St Katharine and Surrey Commercial Docks would have cost a vast amount of money and in the long run it would not have been money well spent. It was much better to make the investment in improving the facilities at Tilbury, down near the mouth of the river, which lent itself more naturally to coping with bigger ships.

And there was another factor that had an important bearing on the enlarging of London's dock facilities. It is one thing to make provision for bigger cargoes and a quicker 'turn-around' for ships, but another to get these increased cargoes to and from the docks. In the old days horse-drawn wagons and carts could transport the piecemeal cargoes of the sailing ships through the narrow streets and alleyways abutting the docks. In more recent times some attempts at street widening have helped to ease the greatly increased traffic back and forth but, by and large, chaos is the word for the traffic situation in London's dockland. How to shift container and unit cargoes through that labyrinth of old-world streets was the problem. The relatively open spaces of the Tilbury area were a much better bet.

So Tilbury it was and with completion of the extension there in 1968, Rennie's and the neighbouring upstream docks were closed. The romantic-sounding West India and East India were to pass out of general parlance and henceforth merely to be something to be read about in books about the history of London. Doomed purely for economic reasons—latterly they had been losing more than £1½ million per year—their quays and warehouses were pulled down by no means because they were derelict. As with his bridges, Rennie had built for posterity. The chief engineer of the Port of London Authority will tell you, 'They took some knocking down.'

As the 1970s started new development was under way. For example, the Central Electricity Generating Board announced in 1971 their plans to build on the forty-five-acre site of the East India dock, at a cost of £50 million, London's largest power station. Twice as big as Battersea, it will have an output of 900 megawatts which, interpreted in layman's terms, is enough to keep going the best part of a million ordinary one-bar electric heaters. And on the twenty-five acres of what was St Katharine Docks work has started on a £25 million project, expected to be finished by 1978, which will transform the site into a complex which will be known as 'St Katharine by the Tower' and which will include an hotel, restaurants, a school, a permanent British trade centre, sports arenas, a yacht basin and other attractions for an anticipated 2,000 new residents.

10 *The Bridge—Man's First Great Engineering Feat*

ALTHOUGH he was to show his talent in all spheres of civil engineering, it is probably on his achievements as a bridge builder that Rennie's reputation mainly rests.

In 1784, at the age of twenty-three, he built his first bridge, across the Water of Leith, about two miles west of Edinburgh, the first bridge on the Edinburgh–Glasgow turnpike road. In all he built sixty-eight bridges, not taking into account all the smaller bridges he built in connection with his extensive work in canal construction. Cyril T. G. Boucher has written of these:

> There are great numbers of them hardly two resembling each other, for all were specially designed for the particular site they occupied, and they have never been touched from the day they were completed. Their architectural effect is very satisfying; most of them are built of stone which, outside the towns, has weathered into tints corresponding to the part of the quarry from which the block concerned was taken. They fit into the landscape so well that they seem to have grown in the places which they occupy, and to have attained organic union with the trees and hedges that link up with them.

At a time when many bridges in the country were of such high-rise construction that the heavy pull up one side and corresponding descent on the other was likened to climbing the roof of a house, the level roadway of Rennie's bridges was regarded as revolutionary. On completion of his bridge across the Esk at Musselburgh, which one still passes over when heading east from Edinburgh, a local who had made his first crossing in his cart was asked what he thought of the town's fine new bridge. 'Bridge?' he said. 'It's na' a bridge. Ye neither ken when ye're on it, nor when ye're off it!'

Rennie's progress south from his Scottish birthplace to the city
he was to make his home can virtually be marked off in bridges he
built, in the Lowlands, the North of England and the Midlands,
culminating in his three great London bridges—Waterloo, Southwark and the one for which the Americans paid £1 million.
Samuel Smiles wrote that Rennie contributed to bridge building
'a series of structures which have not been surpassed in any age or
country' and to appreciate where he fits into the broad sweep of
the evolution of the bridge it should be helpful to trace its
beginnings, to outline its development from the earliest days of
massive but not ungracious masonry to today's 'slimline' structures
of steel and concrete.

Joseph Gies, in his very readable book *Bridges and Men*
(Cassell, 1963), has written: 'Few of man's inventions are more
basic than the bridge. The oldest engineering work devised by
man, it is the only one universally employed in his pre-civilized
state.'

Stepping-stones for primitive man to get across a stream, are
so obviously the earliest form of bridge that they are hardly worth
mentioning. Slabs of stone placed across the stepping-stones to
provide more secure footing for the old and infirm and for those
carrying loads indicate that a bit more thought had been given to
the matter. Then, at places where wider streams had to be
traversed, the erecting of piers consisting of piles of stones upon
which much longer slabs were laid, the whole bonded merely by
the dead weight of the stone, heralded a more sophisticated type
of bridge building. Examples of these are still to be seen, such as
the Postbridge over the East Dart in Devon and Tarr Steps at
Exmoor in Somerset, and there is no reason why these should not
be several thousand years old.

As elementary as the stepping-stones was the fallen tree-trunk
across a creek, either lodged there through a gale-force wind
blowing in the right direction or manhandled into position, to
form what is in basic definition, a bridge: 'a passage across an
impediment'. But in the jungles of South America when a river
was too wide for a tree trunk or too deep or fast-flowing for
stepping-stones, the locals had to be more ingenious. Fording the
river or ferrying across was not always practical. Readily at hand,
however, there were invariably plenty of lianas, the high-climbing
vine strong enough to support the heaviest of men. Tarzan-like,
the traveller would swing out and over the river. No doubt mainly
because of the more timid, a safer, less acrobatic version was
developed whereby several lianas were twined together for added

strength and looped as a permanent sling across the river. Loops were attached to this and the traveller would firmly secure himself to one of these loops. Then, swinging down one side of the long, dangling sling, his impetus would be sufficient to carry him up the other side and on to the far bank. It was not long before someone thought of walking across the suspended vine, tight-rope style, his passage made safe by guide lines attached to prevent it from swaying too much and lengths of liana each side to act as handrails. These could be called the first suspension bridges.

All these primitive bridges served well enough for limited requirement—i.e., the passage of people or packhorses and other such beasts of burden. But then along came the wheel and with it far greater loads to be carried and resultant headaches for the bridge-builders. As Joseph Gies puts it:

> The invention of the wheel with its dramatic train of carts, wagons, roads, highways, merchants, wealth, towns and cities, brought the problem of river crossing to the fore. The invention that solved the bridge problem of ancient civilisation ranks second only to the wheel. It is the arch.
>
> How this marvel came into being is as deep a mystery as the origin of the wheel. Engineers discount the older guess that man built arches in imitation of nature, for the natural arch formed by erosion is structurally quite different from the stone arch. Another guess, that bridging of streams by dumping rocks led to a sudden insight, also is far-fetched.

Archaeologists (notably Taylor in 1854 and Hall and Woolley in this century) have uncovered arches in tombs and underground temples dating back to 4000 B.C. at Ur and elsewhere in ancient Sumer, the earliest Tigris-Euphrates civilization. The Egyptians also were using arches by the year 3000 B.C. But Gies explains:

> Restricted to what amounted to a decorative role in tombs, temples and palaces, the arch existed for at least 2000 years before it was ever used as a bridge. For its serious application the stone arch, like many other Greek, Persian and Egyptian inventions, awaited the coming of the pragmatic, inartistic, strangely gifted Romans.

In the seventh century B.C. the Tarquins, Etruscan Kings of Rome, got engineers to solve the ever persistent problem of sewage disposal by building that system of main drainage that was centuries ahead of its time—the Cloaca Maxima—and since it is still in existence today one can see there the oldest of all Roman stone arch structures.

Up to this time the bridges upon the Tiber and its tributaries had been wooden, including the Pons Sublicius which Horatius defended, to much ensuing publicity. But shortly after the construction of the Cloaca Maxima a bridge called the Pons Solarus, for crossing the Teverone tributary of the Tiber, was built and with this the Romans started their application of the stone arch to bridge building.

At least five of the early Roman stone arch bridges on the Tiber are still standing, in much repaired state and one such is the Pons Fabricus, built in the consularship of Cicero in 62 B.C. and named after the Rome Commissioner of Works of the time but now called the Ponte Quattro Capi, in view of the four-headed figure on the bridge. On their journeys of conquest the Romans built many such bridges, although for some reasons there remains little to be seen in Britain of this sphere of their activity. Elsewhere in Europe, however, there are still extant such Roman bridges as the Pons Augustus in Rimini, Trajan's Bridge over the Danube, the Puente Alcantara and the Segovia aqueduct in Spain, and the celebrated double bridge, the Pont du Gard in southern France.

With the dwindling of the power of Rome after the fourth century no Roman bridges were built. Bridge engineering, along with road engineering and almost every other kind of engineering, disappeared from Europe for several hundred years.

But in medieval times the stonemasons were to build some great bridges, as famous as the Pont d'Avignon, the Ponte Vecchio and the one that has the closest bearing on our subject—Old London Bridge, which was opened in 1209 and was to give more than six hundred years of service before John Rennie was called upon to design a new bridge for the site.

As far as bridges were concerned, Rennie was the last of the great stone men.

In simple terms, the fundamental thing about the stone arch bridge was that it was the stones that held the bridge up and they were seen to hold it up. Blocks of stone were placed one on the other to form the curve of the arch, with the keystone dropped in at the top. Provided the width of each pier on which it stood was at least a third of the span of the arch, it would hold up, with or without benefit of mortar. This was how it had been done for centuries, but from Rennie's time onwards came the transition whereby it was not the stones themselves that held the bridge up.

It was a framework which did that job and the stones were used merely as facing.

Although obvious to an architect, not everybody realizes that there are two basic ways of building a structure, be it a bridge, house, office block or whatever. One is to build 'brick on brick' where the walls themselves hold the thing upright. The other is to build a frame which supports the whole structure, and the walls can be of anything at all—timber, glass, plastic, even tarpaper—since they are not called upon to do any of the work of bearing the weight. An easy way to illustrate this is to compare an egg to the human body. What holds the egg up is its outside wall, but our skin certainly doesn't keep us on our feet—the framework of bone and muscle inside does that.

So apart from short-lasting timber structures, from Roman times on the bridges were stone arch affairs built brick on brick, and the only reason the engineers did not go in for the other type of construction was simply because there was no material available with which to build a strong, durable framework. The Industrial Revolution, the period into which Rennie was born, changed all that. The majority of his bridges were of stone in the centuries-old tradition, and it was only towards the end of his bridge-building career that he made use of the newly developed cast and wrought iron that had come with the Industrial Revolution.

The transition from stone to metal in the construction of bridges started with the completion in 1779 of Thomas Pritchard's bridge over the Severn at Coalbrookdale—the first iron bridge. Thomas Telford, a contemporary of Rennie, used iron for many of his bridges and as we shall see, Rennie himself, although the great 'stone man', built his Southwark Bridge of iron to get the larger spans required at that narrow part of the Thames congested with river navigation. With the coming of the railway era in Victorian times engineers such as Isambard Kingdom Brunel were accused of being 'iron mad'. Iron bridges, in conjunction with the rush of railway expansion, sprang up all over Britain. But iron came to be regarded as a 'dead end material'.

Sir Henry Bessemer having perfected his process of converting cast iron directly into steel in 1870, the iron bridge gradually became a thing of the past. Instead there came into being impressive steel structures such as the characteristically shaped Firth of Forth railway bridge of 1890, still Britain's longest cantilever bridge with its two main spans 1,710 feet long. The Quebec Bridge over the St Lawrence, completed in 1917, took its place as the longest cantilever bridge span (1,800 feet) in the world.

Meanwhile, however, at Brooklyn, New York, they had explored very successfully another aspect of the use of steel in bridge construction. It was found that steel wire cables, used in suspension bridges instead of solid steel girders, offered what is technically known as a much better ratio of strength to weight. Brooklyn suspension bridge, opened in 1883, was an outstanding forerunner of this type of construction. The vast spans which could be achieved with a bridge of this sort brought forth the spectacular Golden Gate bridge in San Francisco, which in 1937 set a record of 4,200 feet with its central span. This was to be bettered by what is currently the world's longest—the Verrazano Narrows Bridge stretching across the entrance to New York City harbour from Staten Island to Brooklyn. This $135 millions project was started in August 1959 and opened to traffic in November 1964, with a span of 4,260 feet. But other steel cable suspension bridges that are planned will gradually raise the world record. A bridge across the Akashi Straits, west of Kobe in Japan, will have a central span of 4,265 feet, followed in due course by the Humber Estuary Bridge (4,850 feet), a 4,600 feet bridge across Tokyo Bay, Japan, and one of 5,000 feet across the Straits of Messina between Sicily and the mainland of Italy.

With bridges thus on the drawing boards with single spans of not far short of a mile, experts have made the staggering announcement that 'with modern materials engineers could build a suspension span two miles long'.

But just as iron overlapped stone construction and steel was being developed while iron bridges were still being built, bridges in another medium have been evolving along with steel.

There was nothing new about concrete. After all, it was something the Romans had been familiar with. But with steel wires or rods incorporated into it to make it 'reinforced concrete' here was virtually a new medium for bridge builders. Today more and more people pass through Berwick-on-Tweed, on the Scottish border, railway closures making it one of the only two routes left if one would go by train into or out of Scotland, which means that more people now have the chance to see what was the first major bridge built of reinforced concrete. Berwick's Royal Tweed road bridge was opened in 1929 to relieve the overworked three-hundred-years-old bridge nearby, a fifteen-arch structure built in the time of James I.

Although reinforced concrete could not rival the gigantic spans of the steel bridges it does have an advantage as far as the up-keep is concerned, for concrete does not demand the constant cleaning and painting that steel demands, as evidenced by the item of information that never ceases to fascinate schoolboys—the fact that no sooner have workmen finished their task of painting the Firth of Forth bridge than it is time to start the job all over again.

By modern standards the Berwick concrete bridge looks ponderous and it is an odd coincidence that the year it was finished, 1928, was the same year in which Eugène Freyssinet over in France perfected his process by which concrete could be greatly strengthened, thus making possible the building of bridges with much more gracious arches. Freyssinet's 'prestressed concrete', which did not have its full impact until the postwar years, is gone into in more detail in the chapter on the building of the new London Bridge that is replacing Rennie's. Suffice it to say here that it created a whole new world as far as concrete bridges were concerned, as can be seen in the proliferation of the 'wafer-thin' arches of the fly-overs, clover-leaves and so on of our motorways of today—the modern equivalent of the dozens of stone bridges Rennie was called upon to build to span the network of canals built in Britain just on two centuries ago.

11 *Waterloo Bridge*

COMPARED to London's present twelve bridges from Tower Bridge to Battersea, there were only three at the beginning of the nineteenth century: Old London Bridge (opened 1209), Westminster (1750) and Blackfriars (1769). They were not adequate for the city which had reached a population of 1,117,290 and into which traffic was flowing much more readily on the newly built turnpike roads and other improved approaches. The construction of the New Road (now Marylebone, Euston and City roads) and the covering of the odorous Fleet River to form Farringdon Street also meant a greater circulation of traffic.

With prosperity streaming in no small measure from West Indian and East Indian trade the early 1800s were a period of much financial speculation or as Smiles more quaintly put it 'a time distinguished for the prevalence of one of these joint-stock fevers which periodically seize the moneyed classes of this country'. A group of speculators formed the Strand Building Company with the object of constructing what would be called the Strand Bridge, to link the Strand near Somerset House with the Surrey side of the Thames at Lambeth. This new bridge, which the shareholders felt would soon pay for itself and bring in a handsome profit from tolls for years hence, would be across the north bend of the river mid-way between the London and Westminster bridges, and not unnaturally those with the controlling interests in these two bridges as well as those concerned with Blackfriars did not welcome the prospect of a newcomer diverting 'passengers' away from them.

Pressure was brought to bear to impede the efforts of the new company, and rivals tried to advance their own schemes for a fourth bridge. One group, with support from a strong lobby in the House of Lords, insisted that a far better plan than building the stone bridge that the Strand company envisaged would be to obviate a large initial outlay by first building a much less expensive wooden bridge, which would in time accumulate enough money from tolls to finance a more substantial one. A wag gave the noblemen in the Lords who backed this scheme the nickname of the 'Wooden Peers'. They failed to get their project accepted and in 1809 the Strand consortium were able to get sanction for their proposal by the necessary Act of Parliament.

The first design they considered was by George Dodds, formerly of the navy, who enjoyed a certain reputation as an engineer and was a pioneer of steam navigation. He was to build a steam-propelled vessel named the *Margery*, which undertook a voyage from its building yards in Glasgow to Dublin and thence by way of the English Channel to London, where it was the first such boat to ply the river and, renamed the *Thames*, was to give Londoners the thrill of going back and forth to Margate by steam navigation. As a bridge designer, however, he proved to be less original.

The managing committee of the bridge company were not satisfied with his design and called in Rennie and William Jessop for their opinion. Son of Josias Jessop, resident engineer of Smeaton's Eddystone Lighthouse, William Jessop had become a ward and pupil of Smeaton on his father's death in 1761 and went on to do outstanding work in the building of canals, notably the Grand Junction Canal, linking the industrial north-west of England with London. He had first become associated with Rennie in dock construction on the Thames at the turn of the century.

Rennie and Jessop subjected the Dodds plan for a fourth London bridge to close scrutiny and pronounced it altogether too derivative. Apart from modifications to fit in with the requirements of the different site, it was nothing more nor less than a copy of the celebrated bridge at Neuilly on the Seine erected some fifty years previously and designed by one of France's greatest bridge builders, Jean Perronet. And Rennie and Jessop did not feel that it was even a good copy. 'We confess', they reported, 'that we do not wholly approve of M. Perronet's construction as adapted for the intended situation. It is complicated in its form and, we think, wanting in effect. The equilibrium of the arches has not been sufficiently attended to. . . .' Following technical details of what they felt were structural faults in the plan, they pointed out that in addition the estimate of cost was quite unrealistic, if not downright misleading.

The Dodds design was not proceeded with. Instead Rennie was commissioned to undertake the task and in June 1810 we find him making a note to the effect that he had accepted direction of the new bridge 'at 1000*l*. for myself and assistants, or 7*l*. 7*s*. a day and expenses; but on no account are any of my people to have to do with the payment or receipt of moneys'.

The bridge he designed to link the street in which he lived, Stamford Street on the south side of the river, to the Strand was to become known as 'Rennie's masterpiece' and was a century after his death to give rise to a bitter controversy that raged for twenty years. It was his very determination to make it not just a bridge but something of outstanding beauty which both earned him acclaim for a masterpiece and was at the root of the controversy.

The setting of the bridge was such that he felt he must do justice in his design to Somerset House, then a much more imposing-looking building that dominated the riverside at what would be the north approach to the new crossing. Today Somerset House is somewhat hidden away amidst modern development, seldom given a second look by commuters hurrying back and forth to Waterloo Station and little more in the public mind now than a synonym for the registration of Births, Deaths and Marriages. But it had an exciting, romantic history before its present prosaic rôle as focal point for researchers from solicitors' offices and private detective agencies, with a special section reserved for those approaching retirement age who require written proof that they are entitled to old age pensions.

The original Somerset House was built to the design of John of Padua, Henry VIII's architect, for Edward Seymour, Duke of Somerset. He was the brother of Jane Seymour, the only one of Henry's luckless wives to bear him a son who survived, and he was made Protector of the young Edward VI. The ambitious Duke, in his desire to make his residence a palace that would rival those at Whitehall and at Hampton Court, plundered numerous churches and other London buildings for stone and was stopped from desecrating St Margaret's Church, Westminster, only by its loyal parishioners driving off his masons 'with clubs and bended bows'. He was prevented from seeing the completion of his palace in 1554 because he was beheaded (a well attended event) and Somerset House was forfeited to the Crown, to become a Royal residence particularly associated with the distaff side. The first woman to occupy it was the young Princess Elizabeth before she ascended the throne and after her time it became the custom to hand this property to the Queen as a dower-house. Anne of Denmark, wife of James I, entertained there, Henrietta Maria held her Catholic court there in the reign of Charles I, and

Catherine of Braganza sought respite there from the gay goings-on of Charles II at Whitehall.

Few of the Royal womenfolk, however, appeared to have had sufficient pride of property to keep Somerset House in good repair and it grew progressively more dilapidated, until in the mid-1700s George III decided it should be pulled down and better accommodation be accorded Queen Charlotte elsewhere. Thus it was that she was given in exchange a charming red-brick Queen Anne house in St James's Park—which was to be developed into Buckingham Palace. At the pulling down of the original Somerset House it was discovered that the Royal ladies, as well as showing a lack of interest in structural repairs, had that other feminine characteristic of not being able to throw anything away, saving pieces of furniture, curtains and knick-knacks that would be 'bound to come in useful some time'. As a result the demolition workers found in attics and storerooms a veritable museum of what had become antiques dating back through three centuries.

The new Somerset House, completed in 1775 and the one we know today, was in keeping with the grand mansions built 'on the strand of the river', by the Earls and Dukes of Northumberland, Norfolk, Bedford, Arundel, Surrey, Essex and so on of which the only reminder now lies in the street-names of the turnings which run down to the river from the Strand.

One of the numerous rôles Somerset House was to undertake over the years was to serve as the home of the Royal Academy and it was not many years prior to Rennie's work on the bridge that the body of Sir Joshua Reynolds had lain in state in one of the great rooms adjoining the spacious courtyard around which the building is set.

In those days there was no Embankment. The Thames was at the bottom of the garden and the noblemen and their families could fish there for salmon[1] and set off from a private jetty up-river to Whitehall or Hampton Court or downstream to Greenwich. The Embankment did not come into being until the 1860s

[1] On 10th February 1971, London newspapers reported that scientists at the National History Museum were thrilled at the capture of a trout at Charlton Wharf, almost as far up the Thames as Greenwich. Although other trout had been caught in recent years in the lower reaches of the Thames, they had been river trout. What excited the scientists was that this new catch was a *sea* trout, which meant that it must have swum up from the estuary. This was a definite breakthrough, tangible evidence that the fight for a cleaner Thames being conducted by the Port of London Authority, the Greater London Council and the Thames Con-

and was not conceived originally as a carriageway and promenade; it was the prosaic and more pressing matter of main drainage that led to its construction. The sewage situation in London having been absolutely appalling for centuries, it was the Victorians who decided to do something drastic about it. Sir Joseph Bazalgette (there is a memorial to him at the foot of Northumberland Avenue) designed London's first efficient main drains and it was merely fortuitous that he came to the conclusion that it would be just as easy and no more costly to build an embankment roadway with sewers underneath as to lay huge pipelines along the foreshore. Thus London got the Victoria Embankment.

This came after Rennie's time and when he was working on his plan for the Strand Bridge the river lapped the frontage of Somerset House, with its much admired row of riverside arches in the Palladian style designed by Sir William Chambers. He wanted his bridge to be as gracious in appearance as these.

He did not design the nine arches in the form of a semi-circle or segment of a circle (the familiar aspect for a bridge arch), but instead made them semi-elliptical and it was this that was one of the things which gave the bridge its much praised beauty.

The shape of these arches based on an ellipse can be seen in the illustration facing p. 104 and in layman's language this is how this pleasing contour is arrived at. A semi-circle we know is half a circle and a segment something less than half. If the lines of such arches continue downwards they will eventually meet and become a full circle. But not so with an ellipse, which can best be described as the shape on a stage when a theatrical spotlight is shone on it—a squashed circle. By cutting across the wide part of this one gets a semi-elliptical (or half an ellipse) shape.

Having designed these aesthetically pleasing arches he further enhanced the appearance of his bridge by adding ornamentation in the form of twin Doric columns at each pier (see illustration) and an idea of the whole effect can be got from a visit to Kelso Bridge in the Scottish Borders, which Rennie built in 1803 and on which he based his ideas for this new one on the Thames. In passing, any who do go to see Kelso Bridge should make note of the lamp standards. They were not in the original design at Kelso. When Rennie's Waterloo Bridge was pulled down the

servancy was bringing results. Significant, said a conservancy officer of the Port of London Authority, 'but I am afraid it is too early yet to hope for a return of those days when the residents of the mansions on the Strand used to fish for salmon at their river frontages'.

people of Kelso saw to it that the lamp standards were brought
north.

In the autumn of 1811 the first excavation for what was to become Waterloo Bridge was made on the north bank at a point
chosen by Rennie between Somerset House and what remained
of the Palace of Savoy, where Eleanor of Provence, one of the
most unpopular Queens in English history, had set up her pack
of rapacious relatives when she came to marry Henry III. On
11th October 1811 a huge block of Cornish granite was ceremoniously laid over the excavation, into which were thrown
bronze, gold and silver coins for a future generation to uncover.

There was much about Rennie's construction of the bridge
that was revolutionary. His was a quite new approach to 'centering', the building of the wooden framework on which the
stones of each arch were laid prior to its removal for them to
stand on their own. Adopted from then on by all other builders
of stone bridges, it requires too much technical detail to be explained here but the illustration facing p. 104 gives an idea of how
the centering was undertaken. Throughout the erecting of the
bridge there were always many watchers from the shore, including Alexander I, Tsar of All the Russias, while on a state visit to
London. He paid more than one visit to the site, pronouncing
himself fascinated.

The granite facings of the bridge were brought from Aberdeen
and Cornwall but the remainder of the stone was hewn in some
fields in Surrey not far from the site and transported in trucks
along a specially built railway. An interesting aspect of this was
that practically all this material was drawn by one horse, 'Old
Jack', who by all accounts was a well-known and very popular
animal. His driver was fond of his drink, especially his 'morning',
which he would have at a pub adjoining the railway track when
other people were having their 'elevenses'. Old Jack would have
to wait outside, sometimes for a lengthy spell if Tom the driver
got wound up with his cronies. On one occasion the horse, being
a conscientious worker, got impatient and poking his head in at
the open door he took his master's coat-collar between his teeth
and pulled him out to resume the day's work.

Rennie's method of surfacing the roadway of the bridge pre-
dated by a number of years the system 'invented' by a fellow-
Scot, John Macadam, who was to become Surveyor-General of
roads in Gloucestershire and in time have his name incorporated
in the language along with those of such men as Plimsoll, Boy-
cott, Shrapnel and Bunsen. As pointed out by Samuel Smiles:

Up to the beginning of the nineteenth century most roads were made with gravel, or flints tumbled upon them in their natural state, and so rounded that they had no points of contact and rarely consolidated. When a heavy vehicle of any sort passed over them their loose structure presented no resistance; the roads were thus constantly standing in need of repair, and they were bad even at the best. The defect did not arise from want of materials, which were not worn out by the traffic but merely displaced.

Smiles wrote of Waterloo Bridge:

The means employed by Mr Rennie forming his road upon the bridge were identical with those adopted by Mr Macadam at Bristol some six years later. When the clay puddle placed upon the intended roadway was sufficiently hard, he spread a stratum of fine screen gravel or hoggins, which was carefully levelled and pressed down upon the clay. This was then covered over with a layer of equally broken flints, about the size of an egg; after which the whole was rolled close together, and in a short time formed an admirable 'macadamised' road. Mr Rennie had practised the same method of making roads over his bridges long before 1809; and he continued to adopt it in all his subsequent structures. But the arrangement constituted so small a part of our engineer's contrivances that, as in many other cases, he made no merit of it.

The bridge was opened on 18th June 1817 by His Royal Highness the Prince Regent (later George IV), attended by 'many distinguished personages', not the least of whom was the Duke of Wellington, the date chosen for the opening being the second anniversary of his successful conclusion of the Battle of Waterloo.

The report in *The Times*, under the terse headline 'WATERLOO-BRIDGE' began: 'On a day remarkable for the fineness of the weather, this noble structure was opened for the public accommodation, with as much splendour and dignity as it is possible to give a ceremony of this description.'

The function began with His Royal Highness arriving by water in the state barge and landing at the stairs on the south-east side. Having declared the bridge officially open he then walked its length with his entourage in procession and embarked on the north-east side, to return up the river. While on the bridge he also announced a change in the name of what until then had always been referred to as the Strand Bridge. *The Times* commented:

This followed the natural and patriotic desire of commemorating, in the most noble public manner, the ever-memorable victory of Waterloo, and afforded a fine opportunity for changing its appellation from that of the street merely into which it opens.

And then the paper added, as if justification were needed:

There are many instances of public works having received their names from events honourable to the country in which they were erected. In late times, Buonaparte, who, with all his vices, had a very shrewd insight into human nature and the external means by which it is worked upon, took advantage of this principle; not simply by his triumphal columns or arches to the honour of Dessaix, of himself, and of his army; but also giving to two new bridges the names of Jena and Austerlitz, where he had gained two decisive victories. But those bridges, however elegant and convenient, are but trifles in civil architecture and engineering when compared with that which was opened yesterday.

We believe there is no bridge in any of the European capitals (and certainly none elsewhere) which is equal, as a great work, to either of the bridges at Westminster or Blackfriars. They are superior works to any of the kind at Paris, Petersburgh, Madrid, Vienna or Dresden, or in the Italian States. But then the Waterloo-bridge is superior to any that bestride the Thames and is consequently the finest in the world. It is a very high testimonial to Mr Rennie, the architect.

Times reporters filled in the colour of the opening day celebrations both at the bridge and on the river, which was crowded with official and private craft, 'the little pleasure vessels of the amateurs of aquatic pleasures enlivening the scene by the neatness and facility of their movements.' They continued:

The bridge was decorated with eighteen standards elevated. In the centre and at each end were two Royal Standards of Great Britain; between them the standards of Russia and the Netherlands and the Orange flag; thus representing the nations the success of whose combined armies occasioned the appellation of Waterloo-Bridge. . . .
A party of Horse Guards from the Battle of Waterloo, and many of them bore on their brave breasts the trophies of their valour, were upon the bridge. . . . Decorations of laurel were worn by the soldiers with 'Waterloo 18th June 1815' in gold letters.

Waterloo bridge showing elliptical arches by T. Shepherd

Centering of arch—Waterloo Bridge

View of the west side of London Bridge in 1823 by Major G. Yates

Southwark Bridge from Bank side by T. Shepherd

Salutes were fired from time to time from twenty-five pieces of artillery aligned on the bridge between 'the lamps on each sidewalk fashioned from 202 cannon taken from the enemy and the firing did not terminate till His Royal Highness had landed at Whitehall watergate and returned to Carlton-House'.

Antonio Canova (1757–1822) Italian sculptor and leader of the classical revival in Italy, described Waterloo Bridge as 'the noblest bridge in the world' and once made the remark that 'it is worth going to England solely to see Rennie's bridge'. It was for this work that Rennie was offered, and declined, the honour of a knighthood.

A century later there was still great admiration for the bridge and on the hundredth anniversary of the laying of its foundation stone the *Observer* in 1910 commented: 'The magnificent edifice known as Waterloo Bridge has ever been and will long remain pre-eminent among the bridges of all ages and all countries. . . . Londoners have, indeed, good reason to be proud of this monumental work of art.'

But 1910 was just at the start of the Petrol Age and when in just a matter of a few years it came into full flood with all its motorized transport Waterloo Bridge was threatened. . . .

Claxton Fidler, engineer of Victorian times, observed that 'the object of every bridge is to resist the "bending moments" of the given load'. By the start of the 1920s Waterloo Bridge's 'given load' had changed radically in nature. Designed for the leisurely traffic of horse-drawn carriages and wagons, it had passed its first century of service only to find itself subjected to the petrol age, with its multiplications of motor cars, vans, lorries and solid-tyred, double-decker buses. In May 1924 a weakening in the foundations of one of the piers was detected and this was to cause a sinking of part of the roadway. The bridge was closed for several months while strengthening of the foundations was carried out and a contract was placed with Sir William Errol and Co. of Glasgow for the building of a temporary bridge. It was put up in twelve months and when the bridge proper was reopened for traffic with wooden planking substituted for the original roadway to ease the weight, its temporary neighbour was left standing in case it should be found that the bridge could not return to full use. As will be seen later, 'temporary' was to prove a misnomer as far as the Errol structure of iron girders was concerned.

In the number of motor vehicles on the road the 1920s saw the most spectacular increase of any decade in England's history. The

330,518 registrations at the end of the First World War had jumped to 2,181,032 in 1929. London's share of this tremendous outpouring of new vehicles from the manufacturing plants on to streets still attuned in the main to the horse-and-buggy days produced unbelievable traffic chaos, and among the worst bottlenecks were those at the river crossings of the metropolis. This especially applied to getting in and out of the West End from the Surrey side of the Thames. By comparison the City was relatively well-served by four bridges—Blackfriars, Southwark, London Bridge and Tower Bridge. The West End had but two. Westminster had had a new bridge built in 1862 replacing the 1750 bridge of Wordsworth's sonnet. And the other, of course, was Rennie's Waterloo Bridge.

By 1930 it became obvious that the pressure must be taken off these two West End bridges and plans were put before Parliament for an Act to authorize the building of a new road bridge between the two at Charing Cross. But the Bill was defeated at this time of retrenchment at the beginning of the Depression.

The focus was then turned to Waterloo Bridge, where one of two things would have to be done. Either it would have to be widened to handle four rather than two 'lines' of traffic (the term 'lines' gave way to the American expression 'lanes of traffic' at about the same time that the British abandoned 'wireless' in favour of America's 'radio'), or the bridge should be scrapped and a new one built in its place.

The controversy that this gave rise to was akin to the verbal battles of today in regard to the site of a new London airport. But it was not local residents versus the planners. On one side were those who wanted to retain Rennie's bridge—eminent architects and engineers not only of London but from all over Britain and even on the Continent, where it was recognized as a masterpiece of bridge building. Ranged with these were the Fine Arts Council and similar organizations. On the other side were the pragmatists—away with the old, there is no room for antiquity if it holds up progress.

The battle of Waterloo Bridge raged in the correspondence columns of *The Times* for a period of years. A typical letter by E. M. Kinstam, K.C., of the Temple, pleaded for the preservation of 'this glory of our blood and state'. Sir Walter Davison, M.P., wrote urging the saving of 'one of the greatest architectural masterpieces we possess'.

But those who argued that the bridge should be kept did not do so purely on aesthetic grounds. A. P. Powys, secretary of the

Society for the Preservation of Ancient Buildings, wrote of the inadvisability of building a new bridge 'at a time when economy and retrenchment are urgently needed', going on to point out that 'for a tithe of the cost the existing structure, one of our greatest national monuments and probably the best stone bridge ever built, can be underpinned, reconditioned and widened'. Others supporting this argument drew attention to the fact that Rennie's bridge could be reconditioned for many more years of service at precisely the amount allocated for pulling it down at the estimated cost of £1,295,000 for demolition and construction of a new bridge.

Another practical consideration was the matter of traffic problems. Arthur Keen, chairman of the Thames Bridge Conference, wrote:

> The leading engineers of our day, having closely examined the bridge, have announced that the danger of collapse is nonexistent . . . all we would get would be a useless new bridge of six lines which would only make the traffic block at the Strand even worse.

The traffic block at the Strand that he alluded to was Wellington Square at the foot of the Aldwych, meeting place for all the traffic from along the Strand, from Kingsway and from Fleet Street. Wellington Square was—and still is—one of London's worst bottlenecks. There was, as now, nothing that could be done about it—unless planners had the courage to get rid of Somerset House, Drury Lane Theatre, the Savoy and Strand Palace hotels and numerous other encumbrances. Why, argued those for the retention of Rennie's bridge, have traffic trying to get across Wellington Square on a six-lane basis from Waterloo Bridge when the problem was creating enough headaches without thus aggravating it?

It became a political issue, a conflict of party politics at its most bitter and lowest level. In 1934 the Labour Party gained control of the London County Council for the first time and, under the leadership of Herbert Morrison, they saw in Waterloo Bridge an opportunity to assert themselves against the Prime Minister Stanley Baldwin.

In 1925 a Royal Commission on Cross River Traffic in London had been set up, primarily to look into the matter of Waterloo Bridge, and in the following year when it delivered its report it recommended the retention of the bridge, with the roadway to be widened to accommodate four lanes of traffic.

But when Labour gained power in the LCC they preferred to quote the view of some engineers in 1925 that the bridge should be taken down to prevent it falling down, rather than the Royal Commission's view to the contrary effect. The opinion of experts who had come forward to support the Commission's findings were dismissed by the spokesman for the LCC's Improvements Committee: 'Those eminent architects writing to the papers to save "Rennie's masterpiece", while eminent as architects, are not experts on traffic.' The Committee, to further their destructive cause, even managed to find their own 'eminent architect' to say that the widening of Rennie's bridge would 'completely mutilate the character of the original design—it would create not only a new bridge but an ugly one'. And the bridge was written off in their minds as 'not a national monument but only a bridge that happens to have a connection with Waterloo because of the presence of the Duke of Wellington at the opening'.

R. C. Norman, of the Tory opposition in the LCC, said:

> . . . There is no advantage in building for six lines or sixty if traffic cannot get on and off a bridge. . . . Waterloo Bridge is the most famous bridge in London, a shapely bridge of international repute and a great many people feel it is the greatest building put up in the nineteenth century. . . . It is, despite what the Improvements Committee say, an historical monument. Had Parliamentary powers to be obtained, they know that they would not get them. The Council will make a tragic and irretrievable mistake if it destroys Waterloo Bridge.

Herbert Morrison summed things up, dealing first with the aesthetic argument:

> I have been watching the correspondence on the subject and think Mr Norman wrong in deciding that a number of letters in *The Times* necessarily constitutes public opinion. The Council should beware of submitting to what amounts to dictation from the architectural profession. There is no absolute standard of beauty in art. Beauty is a matter for individual decision and I am not going to delegate to the Royal Institute of British Architects or anybody else my right to decide for myself what is beautiful.

And then on the more familiar ground of party politics:

> I do not care a rap for the views of the Royal Commission. It reported what it wanted to report. It was appointed by a Government that had made up its mind that Waterloo Bridge

has got to stay and I believe that Mr Baldwin in appointing as Chairman a man who signed the petition in favour of retaining the bridge did something he ought never to have done.

Under his leadership the Labour-dominated LCC became set on pressing party politics to its ultimate. They decided to present the Government with a *fait accompli*. On 21st June 1934 Morrison in person ceremoniously wielded the sledge-hammer to dislodge the first stone in the demolition of the bridge. Confronted with Waterloo Bridge literally coming down, Parliament hastened to take legal advice as to the London County Council's power to act of its own accord in this regard. The ruling went against them. The fresh outcry that this evoked seemed now of no avail.

Such was the public interest in the controversy that in the latter part of 1935 one Macbeth Elliott brought out an illustrated booklet published by Gibbs, Bamford and Co., of Luton, and entitled *Waterloo Bridge: Its Swan Song*. If not actually a whitewash of Herbert Morrison, it did its best to justify his actions. The author described Rennie as 'the son of a well-known Scottish farmer but to his own abilities and push is due the high position he filled in the engineering world'. The publication was 'Dedicated with Admiration to Herbert Morrison' and in the course of describing the swinging of the hammer to start the demolition the author wrote: 'Posterity, if not all today, will thank Herbert Morrison abundantly for having the courage to face facts.'

Just how acrimonious the situation was is indicated by the fact that to show their displeasure at what the Socialists of the LCC had done, Parliament refused to contribute towards the cost of the new bridge. It was four years before feelings had simmered down sufficiently for Parliament to relent to the extent of making a grant of £300,000.

Demolition took two years through into 1936, with the 'temporary' iron girder bridge put up ten years before continuing to do service at that crossing. Bits and pieces of Rennie's bridge found their way to all parts of the United Kingdom. Some of the lights, as mentioned, were fitted to Kelso Bridge. The granite balusters, of which there were no fewer than 1,296 in the balustrades on each side of the top of the bridge, were seen to be ideal to act as stands for sundials or bird baths. As mentioned earlier there is one incorporated into the ghastly design of the Rennie memorial and another is placed in the garden of Phantassie House.

During demolition the coins that had been placed under the foundation stone in 1811 were found. They were in a glass container (broken by the pickaxe of the workman who uncovered them) and each of the thirteen coins had been wrapped in oiled linen, so that they were in perfect condition. There was a guinea piece of 1794, a silver groat of 1800 and, dating from 1787 to 1811, bronze and silver to the value of five shillings and five- and ten-shilling pieces in gold.

The bulk of the dismantled stone—sixty thousand tons of it—was taken to Morgan's stonemason's yard in Harmondsworth, Middlesex, for storage while the LCC sought a buyer. It was an impressive sight for anyone passing by in that area—twelve great heaps of massive blocks of stone, each pile fifty to sixty feet in height, set out on the thirteen-acre area of the yard. With the rental mounting up without the LCC being able to find a buyer for it *in toto*, Morgan's were able to buy it from them 'for a song' and bringing in stone-cutting machinery they set about selling it piecemeal.

Alf Payne, contracts manager of the stone division of Limmer Holdings, the firm which was eventually to take over the disposal of the stone, will tell you, with the nostalgia of a man who has been a stonemason all his working life, that it was 'the best' and affectionately reel off the names of the various types such as brown Bramley and pink Bramley, Scottish flecked Craigleith and Welsh blue pennant.

The purchasers, usually at a price of around forty shillings per cubic yard, were mainly contractors needing stones for the facings of walls and bridges, office blocks and private homes. Much of it can be seen now in Monmouthshire in new bridgework across the River Wye on the Ross to Monmouth road. Another big contract involved sending up to the Maglashan firm in Scotland two hundred tons a week for two years—more than twenty thousand tons of stone for use in the building of railway viaducts between Edinburgh and Glasgow. In houses throughout the British Isles there are hundreds of fireplaces with colourful stone surrounds which have a link with Rennie's Waterloo Bridge. In cemeteries there are gravestones of what Mr Payne describes as 'the rugged type' which have been fashioned from the stone. Typical of these smaller purchases was the occasion when an elderly woman came into the office at the yard and said that when her husband had been vicar of Harmondsworth Church she had passed by the huge heaps of stone every day; could she have a piece for his gravestone?

Today there is little left of the stone Rennie accumulated for use in the building of his Waterloo Bridge. The time came, in April 1970, when the land on which it stood was of more value than what remained of the stone itself. Since then it is being crushed up for use as fill-in under asphalt and concrete roadways. 'It is sad,' says Alf Payne, 'to see that beautiful stone subjected to this gruesome treatment.'

The new Waterloo Bridge designed by Sir Giles Scott to replace Rennie's was of five arches, with one across the Victoria Embankment, and it was to be the first all-concrete bridge to span the Thames. It was intended that it would be completed in 1940 but there was an interruption. Work carried on despite the war, enemy action adding to the delays caused by shortage of materials and labour. In September 1940 part of the new structure was destroyed in an air raid and had to be rebuilt but it was at length 'one of the few great improvements made to the London scene in wartime'.

Opened for traffic in Sepember 1942, it was finished in December 1944. Morrison, who by then had accepted a knighthood, formally opened the bridge on 10th December 1945 and today those who make the crossing can see this fact recorded on the stonework at the northern end of the bridge.

Directly below, however, there is something far more rewarding to look at. When you walk along the Victoria Embankment and come to Waterloo Bridge, the first arch of which spans the road, you will notice that the parapet between you and the river stops and does not resume again until some fifty feet ahead. In this gap there is what seems at first glance to be just a rough pile of masonry on a level with the parapet. Perhaps the foundation for something that was not completed? Even on the brightest of days it is somewhat gloomy down there under the bridge but if you look more closely you will learn that some sentimentalist in the LCC must have insisted that something of Rennie's Waterloo Bridge should be left for future generations to see. It is in fact the base of the first pier of Rennie's original bridge, the rest of which was demolished by 1936. The solidity of the massive blocks of stone can be seen, the shape of the twin Doric columns that extended up to the causeway of the bridge, the concentration of 'in-fill' stones and mortar packed into the foundations. Set a few yards out in the water is a row of metal piles driven into the bed of the river and serving as a barricade to prevent passing craft colliding with what remains of the pier. But there is no plaque or anything else to let passers-by know that left standing there, *in situ,* is part of what was regarded as one of the world's great bridges.

The 'temporary' bridge which had been built beside Waterloo Bridge when it was undergoing repair in 1926 and which since September 1942 had been used merely by pedestrians was dismantled in November 1943 after seventeen years of faithful service to Londoners. But that was not the end of it. Its huge girders were shipped downstream and stored in a warehouse, the LCC employees who did the work being puzzled as to what was intended for them. They were even more puzzled when workmen started building extra sections. The only people who knew what it was all about were a handful of those higher up in the LCC, who were undertaking hush-hush negotiations with the Ministry of Supply and the War Office.

This was months before D-Day but when in time Antwerp was captured the whole dismantled bridge down to the last nut and bolt was shipped across the Channel and through Belgium in specially adapted railway trucks. The Germans destroyed the Rhine bridges and only the one across the river at Remegen was in Allied hands. When it collapsed, there ready to be put up in its place was the assemblance retrieved from the temporary Waterloo Bridge. Engineers did an heroic job erecting it under fire and within a week the bogged-down tanks, guns and trucks were rolling—thanks to some far-seeing boffins in the War Office.

12 *Southwark Bridge*

IN the early 1800s such was the demand for further bridges across the Thames to augment the three in existence (London, Blackfriars and Westminster) that while Rennie was working on his Waterloo Bridge he was commissioned to do two others.

His Vauxhall Bridge on the site of the modern one, which was built in 1906, was never completed. His son Sir John in his autobiography wrote of it in part:

> About this period, viz. the year 1813, having obtained a tolerable knowledge of the rudiments of my profession of engineering, both theoretical and practical, my father determined to place upon my shoulders a certain degree of responsibility, and put me under the direction of that late worthy and excellent man, Mr James Hollingsworth, whom my father had appointed to resident engineer at Waterloo Bridge, which was then building. I felt the responsibility of this office a good deal, and entered upon it with every determination and desire to meet my father's approbation; and during the inclement winter of 1813–14, when the frost lasted about two months, and the Thames above London Bridge was frozen over for several weeks, I was obliged to attend the piling of the foundations of the first and second piers on the Surrey side of the river night and day for three days each week, which severely tried my constitution.
>
> At this period Vauxhall Bridge was also in course of construction, and I was directed by my father to attend to this also, under Mr Jones, the resident engineer; but they had scarcely finished the Middlesex abutment up to the springing of the first arch, and were preparing the caisson for founding the first pier, when the Company found they had not sufficient funds to carry into effect Mr Rennie's design, which was very beautiful.

Concurrently Rennie was engineer-in-chief to another company,

formed in 1813, to build a crossing at a point between London
Bridge and Blackfriars and to be called Southwark Bridge.

In view of all Rennie's commitments on the Thames at this
period it should be explained how it came about that so many
companies were being formed to build bridges over London's
river that it was like investors of today scurrying around to form
consortiums to try to get commercial television franchises. Back in
those days, as with turnpike roads, money was to be made from
tolls on bridges. It was a field open to private enterprise where in
the same way as the great commercial television networks today,
bridge companies of the early nineteenth century sought and were
granted monopolies in their particular areas. It was not in fact
until the 1870s that London's bridges were freed of tolls. London,
Blackfriars, Westminster and Waterloo were the first to be taken
over by local authorities and made free to the public and then by
Act of Parliament in 1877 the remainder were freed from tolls.
As a reminder of how things used to be, the toll houses at each end
of the Albert Bridge were left standing.

That the building of a Thames bridge in the old days was a
profitable investment can be seen from a study of the statements
of accounts that have been preserved. In 1849, for example, we
see that the proprietors of Waterloo Bridge were able to announce
that the half-yearly revenue from tolls up to February of that
year amounted to £10,101 16s., enabling them to declare a divi-
dend of 4s. 4d. in the pound.

Each person who used one of the bridges was issued with a toll
receipt to be surrendered on the other side and there are samples
of these from Southwark and Waterloo bridges to be seen at the
Guildhall Library. They are about two inches square and of a
different colour for each day. Also still in in existence is the table
of charges displayed on the toll gates. Broken up into twenty-
eight categories it covered practically everything that moved and
was likely to make use of the bridge. In part it read:

TOLLS TO BE TAKEN AT THE BRIDGE
FOR EACH TIME OF PASSING

	s.	d.
For every Foot Passenger		1
For every Coach, Berlin, Landau, Vis-a-Vis, Chariot, Chaise, Calash and Pleasure Carriage having 4–3 wheels drawn by 6 Horses or other Beasts	1	6
Ditto drawn by 4 Horses or other Beasts	1	0
Ditto drawn by less than 4 horses and more than 1 Horse or other Beast		6

Ditto drawn by 1 Horse or other Beast		4
For every Wagon, Dray or such other 4-wheel Carriage drawn by 6 or more horses or other Beasts	1	0
For every 2-wheeled Carriage drawn by 1 Horse or other Beast		2
For every additional Horse drawing such Carriage		1
For every Horse, Mare, Gelding, Mule, Ass laden or not laden and not drawing		1½
For every drove of Oxen or neat Cattle, per score		8
For every drove of Calves, Hogs, Sheep or Lambs per score		4

Apart from the meticulous detail of the above and other lists ensuring that all eventualities were covered, one gets a good idea of the type of traffic Rennie's bridges were designed for and how the coming of age of motorized transport, which could not have been foreseen at that time, made quite different demands on the structures.

The Southwark Bridge Company, having been granted their franchise by Act of Parliament, found themselves in difficulty from the outset. Since the bridge was to span the narrowest part of the river the Corporation of London and the Conservators of the Thames raised objections on the grounds that the bridge would obstruct navigation. They insisted that it would have to provide the greatest possible waterway, in other words have few piers and high broad arches.

To meet this stipulation Rennie, the last of the great stone bridge builders, had to turn his attention to the use of cast iron to gain bigger spans and thus he became one of the pioneers in the construction of the iron bridges which were to proliferate with the coming of the Railway Age in early Victorian times. His iron bridge at Southwark was of course not the first major structure of this type. As we have seen earlier the one at Coalbrookdale over the Severn completed in 1779 was the epoch-making bridge of this type of construction. Sunderland's bridge at Wearmouth, built in 1796, was the second and it was noteworthy for having the largest cast iron arch—236 feet. This record was to go, however, with Rennie's design at Southwark which called for three arches, two of 210 feet span and the centre one of 240 feet.

Even we laymen can by now grasp the fact that the broad sweep of these arches, which were flat segments of a circle, would cause much more pressure outwards (laterally) than the narrower (120 feet) elliptical arches of Waterloo Bridge, where there was more downward pressure. Therefore the abutments (the founda-

tions on each side of the river) at the Southwark bridge had to be
specially constructed to offer the maximum resistance to this
lateral pressure. The stones were to be set at an angle, so that in
effect the line of the arch was continued down into the depths of
the foundations and it was felt necessary that they should be huge
blocks of granite each weighing from fifteen to twenty tons.

How these massive pieces of stone were obtained is told by
Sir John in his autobiography, and what follows gives a good
picture of the demanding sort of work he and his father and the
other engineers of the time had to undertake in merely getting
the *material* for their projects.

These blocks of stone were of such unusual magnitude, and
nothing of the kind had been used in London, or even elsewhere in England, that the contractors made considerable
objection to obtaining them, and even went so far as to say
that it could not be done. I was perfectly convinced that it
could be done, and that it was merely a question of a little
extra expense, and strongly recommended my father to insist
upon it, as it was absolutely necessary for the security of the
bridge; and he did so, and directed me to proceed to Aberdeen for the purpose of obtaining them. I accordingly started
for Aberdeen; and when there found that all the quarries had
only been opened up on a small scale, and were merely adapted
for getting paving stones, the commerce of which with London
was then upon a considerable scale; but the idea of obtaining
blocks of the size required for Southwark Bridge was considered to be entirely out of the question. I therefore determined to proceed to Peterhead, thirty miles farther northward,
where the red granite abounds in large masses near the coast,
and where I was told I should probably succeed; but still, they
said, even there it would be very difficult to get them.

Upon arriving at Peterhead I immediately set to work ex-
ploring the adjacent country for several miles around, and soon
found that blocks of the size required could readily be obtained,
and even larger ones if necessary. I accordingly selected, by
way of experiment, a mass of solid rock about four miles to
the south of Peterhead, lying within a quarter of a mile of the
sea coast, and about 200 feet above the main turnpike road to
Peterhead, which ran along the sea shore. This block, weighing
about twenty-five tons, was accordingly marked out, and was
soon detached from the main mass of rock by means of wedges,
and was ten feet long by five feet square. The workmen who
executed this task were rewarded with ample wages and a
good supply of whisky, and were extremely proud of their
achievement. Then came the important question, how they

were to convey it to Peterhead. To get it to the turnpike road was soon accomplished by means of a wooden inclined tramway formed of stout planks moved upon wooden rollers. Good wages and whisky settled this, and the workmen considered it a further great triumph; but still the greater difficulty remained, how to get this vast block (as it was then considered) four miles to Peterhead.

I went back to Peterhead and after numerous inquiries, and as many failures and objections on all sides, at last found two large single bogies, each consisting of a pair of strong wheels eight feet in diameter, connected by a strong axle shaft and a double pair of shafts in front. These two pairs of wheels I joined together at the axle shafts by two strong beams, cased with wrought iron, and strengthened the wheels and axles in other respects as far as necessary. I then took this carriage to the block of red granite already mentioned lying in the road, and slung the stone, by means of strong chains, to the two longitudinal bearers of the carriage. Some twelve or fourteen horses were then attached to the carriage, and off we departed in great triumph to Peterhead. The toll-keeper, never having seen such a mass of stone before, did not know what to charge. However, having at length satisfied his demand, we proceeded onwards, and we had scarcely advanced a mile when we came to a soft piece of road, which yielded under the great weight of the stone, and the wheels stuck fast, buried about nine inches in the ground. This accident created general dismay amongst the attendant workmen, and they began to consider the task hopeless. However, nothing daunted by this mischance, I soon rallied their courage, and with plenty of screw-jacks, wedges and levers judiciously applied, we raised the wheels out of the ground, and placed strong beams under them, forming a rough kind of railway, over which we dragged and pushed the carriage with its stone in safety, until we passed the unsound part of the road. This operation detained us about a day. Everybody worked with the greatest ardour and goodwill, which was aided not a little by a plentiful supply of whisky, and the men were determined, for the honour of Scotland, that they would not be beaten. Having overcome this serious obstacle, we started again on our journey, and reached Peterhead about four hours afterwards, making the total length of the journey —four miles—a day and a half. The whole town of Peterhead, having never seen such a sight before, turned out to see us, and welcomed us with the most enthusiastic acclamations.

The next thing was to get a vessel that would take this monstrous block of stone, as it was termed, to London; and although there were a considerable number of vessels in the harbour, I could not at first prevail upon any of the captains to take the charge. All sorts of objections were made, and amongst the rest, it was impossible to get the stone on board, and if they did, it would make a hole in the bottom, and the vessel would founder with all on board. At last, after a great deal of difficulty, I found a brig of about 200 tons burthen, the captain of which, after a good deal of persuasion, consented to take the block of stone to London, provided that I would put it on board at my own risk and expense, and indemnify him against all risk or loss on the voyage, which I accordingly agreed to do.

Then came the last important question, how was the block to be got on board? There was no crane in the port capable of lifting above two or three tons.

I immediately set to work to supply this deficiency by means of two sets of strong sheer-poles, capable of bearing ten to fifteen tons each. The vessel engaged was accordingly brought alongside the quay where a crane was fixed, so that it should nearly plumb the centre of the hatchway of the vessel, which it was necessary to enlarge and strengthen considerably before it could receive the stone. I then secured the sheer-poles well at the top, and placed one set on each side of the crane, a short distance from the extremity of each end of the hatchway. The legs of the sheer-poles were firmly fixed in the bed of the harbour, striding over the vessel, so that they were perfectly independent of the vessel, and the top of each pole was directly over the centre of the hatchway. To the top of the sheer-poles I applied a pair of strong treble sheave-blocks, capable of receiving a thick rope; each block was worked by a double purchase crab or windlass manned by eight men each, besides four to work the crane, so that the block would be suspended at three points, the sheers taking the greatest weight. From the quay a strong timber gangway was constructed over the hatchway, the outer end being supported, clear of the vessel, by piles driven into the bed of the harbour on each side, in order that the ship might be kept perfectly steady until the stone was placed within the hold, because otherwise the stone resting on any part of the deck might have upset it.

Everything being ready, the stone was brought alongside the vessel and the tackle of the crane and of the two pairs of sheer-poles was made fast to three sets of strong chains fastened round the stone, which was transferred upon rollers over the centre of the hatchway of the vessel, the purchases of the crane and the sheer-poles being kept sufficiently tight so as to prevent any undue pressure upon the platform, when I heard a crack; in fact, one of the sheer-poles had bent and partially yielded; it was then blocked and, the sheers having been first spliced with strong rope, the stone was again hoisted and swung clear of the platform, which was removed, and the stone was lowered into the hold of the vessel and properly secured without any further delay or accident.

The whole of these operations were witnessed with intense interest by many of the inhabitants of Peterhead, and when so successfully completed the quays resounded with cheers. The gallant workmen who laboured so arduously and with such goodwill, and to those whose exertions the success may be mainly attributed, were plenteously regaled, together with their friends, with all the good things Peterhead afforded, in which the worthy inhabitants joined, and the remainder of the day was passed in mutual goodwill and festivity.

Sir John asked the reader's indulgence for having gone into such detail about getting the big piece of stone on ship to London and explained that at the time 'operations of this kind had not been attempted, and were entirely novel, and were considered extraordinary'. Quick to anticipate that the Egyptians would at once come to mind, he concluded his description of the work with the comment:

It is true that many centuries before the Egyptians had shown the way; but then the whole power and resources of the nation had been devoted to this object, and incredible sums of money and great labour had been expended, regardless of the misery and oppression of the people. But in Great Britain it has been considered a true axiom of political economy, that every article should be produced at the least possible cost, and no work should be undertaken unless it would yield a fair profit for the capital expended.

Before leaving the subject of son John getting the Peterhead granite for his father's bridge at Southwark it is worth digressing for a moment to show that for the industrious engineers of those days it was not all work and no play. As Rennie's son tells it:

Whilst at Peterhead, my father gave me an introduction to his old and intimate friend, the well-known James Ferguson, of Pitfour, the member for the county and the intimate friend of Mr Pitt. Mr Ferguson possessed a large fortune and was so fond of Mr Pitt that it is believed that if Mr Pitt had survived him he intended to have made him heir to his estates. Mr Ferguson rarely, if ever, spoke in the House of Commons, but when he

did it was always to the purpose; his speeches, although exceedingly short, were replete with much common sense,
accompanied by a terseness of wit, humour and drollery, which
convulsed his hearers with laughter. He used always to say
that he had heard 'mony a gude speech but it never changed
my vote, I aye voted with Mr Pitt'. He was an old bachelor
of the most amiable and charitable disposition, beloved by
everybody and universally popular throughout the county.
Pitfour was 'Liberty Hall' and was open to all comers, the only
limit being the amount of sleeping accommodation.

As illustrative of the manners of those days, I will simply
mention that when I presented my father's letter of introduction he received me most kindly and invited me to spend a few
days under his most hospitable roof, which I accepted, and on
the first day there was assembled a large party of the most
influential gentlemen of the county; as was usual wines of all
kinds flowed in abundance and universal hilarity prevailed. To
give some idea of his hospitality, Mr Ferguson seldom had less
than thirty-six pipes, a measure of wine equal to 126 gallons
of fine port wine in his cellars, besides claret, burgundy, sherry,
champagne, brandy and whisky, in proportion. The consequence was that not long after dinner several of the guests fell
off their chairs and took their nap under the table, from which
after a short time they recovered and resumed their seats, and
again set to work on their potations, which continued until long
past midnight; by this time another considerable batch of
guests were under the table, leaving their glasses full. In this
manner the evening passed merrily away, and it was late in the
morning before the whole of the company found their way to
their beds.

At that time the younger Rennie had been still only in his
teens, which gives a good indication of the faith Rennie had in
the young man's ability to keep up with his elders—at work *and*
play.

The stone from Peterhead in due course found its way by sea
down the coast to the Thames site to join the other assembled
masonry from the Craigleith Quarry near Edinburgh, from Dundee, Yorkshire and Cornwall, and the ironwork cast at the Walker
foundry in Rotherham.

The sections of iron for each of the three arches were put in
place and bolted together on the support of a temporary wooden
'centering' in precisely the same way as in the building of a stone
arch. The completed arches with this support under them were
left to stand thus for several days, during which time Rennie got

his workmen to subject the whole structure to the minutest search of every part to ensure that no defect could be discovered before the great moment—the withdrawal of the wooden 'framework' under each arch. The removal of all the timber occupied a week and then with the iron arches standing entirely on their own the vital measurements were made. It was found that the two smaller arches had subsided by two inches and the main arch two and a half inches—exactly as calculated.

During the putting in place of the superstructure, which brought the total weight of iron used in the bridge to 3,732 tons, and the final laying of the pre-Macadam macadamized roadway as at Waterloo Bridge, Rennie carried his meticulous attention to detail to the extent of having a variety of gauges attached to the arches to measure the effects of the climate on the ironwork. Through the summer and winter months observations were made daily, in the morning, at midday and at sunset. It was found that 'the variation in the rise and fall of the crown of the arches was one-tenth of an inch for every ten degrees of temperature, so that taking the extremes of temperature at London to be ten degrees below freezing point at Fahrenheit in winter, and eighty degrees in summer, the utmost rise and fall of the arches may be taken at seven-tenths, or at most one inch'. However, in view of the fact that 'any variation in temperature, unless continued for some time, has no sensible effect upon such a large mass of iron, in our variable climate, the rise and fall of the crowns of the arches may be taken upon the average somewhat below the amount stated', and therefore it was felt that there could be no cause for concern in this regard.

With the bridge nearing completion in 1818 there was an interesting sidelight on the difference between father and son. Having been given a measure of responsibility in supervising the construction, young John felt that 'as this was considered a work of great importance I was highly honoured by my father's confidence and devoted my energies to it with the greatest anxiety and with a determination to do everything in my power to make it successful'. However, in August 1818, 'having worked very hard, I may say almost night and day, for some time, I was nearly worn out and I decided to take a holiday', something which was apparently quite alien to his father. The son wrote of his holiday:

I therefore determined to go to Belgium and visit the celebrated field of Waterloo, which closed the long and eventful revolutionary war, and attracted the admiration and interest of the whole civilised world. I accordingly started for Dover, in company with my old friend, Mr Joseph Gwilt, architect, and crossed over to Calais. . . . We had been so considering the French as our deadly foes that we could hardly believe ourselves to be at peace with them, and to be actually in France and so civilly treated by them. . . .

On the next morning we started for the scene of the celebrated battle of Waterloo. In this place, like every Englishman, I took the greatest possible interest, and pictured to myself the whole of that terrific and stirring scene as being enacted before me. Nothwithstanding the lapse of time since that battle had taken place considerable traces of it were still visible, particularly in the blood-stained walls and ruined, desolate and half-consumed buildings of the keys of the position, Hougemont and La Haye Sainte, and the remnants of shakos, arms and military clothing which strewed the field on all sides, and the fresh-made graves, where many thousand gallant fellows lay entombed. The whole field and neighbouring villages were crowded with guides to explain the different particulars of that memorable struggle and to sell the numerous articles they had raked up from the field of battle; we bought some of these as mementoes and wandered for hours over every part of the field of desolation, until we fancied that we had mastered every detail of the conflict, and were almost fit to take the command of an army ourselves. We then returned to Brussels, highly gratified and instructed by the excursion.

The holiday was continued elsewhere on the Continent. Meanwhile Rennie senior at home continued with the carrying through of the Southwark Bridge project, plus, to name only some of the other undertakings he was at work on that year, a new bridge at Rochester, Regent's Park sewer, designs for a cast-iron bridge in Naples, report and recommendations for Yarmouth Harbour, and steam-driven machinery for paper-making for Bank of England notes. It has been said of Rennie by Boucher, that 'his only known holiday was taken in 1816 when he spent a month touring the Continent with James Watt, junior, but even this was something of a busman's holiday for he seems to have spent most of the time looking at docks, harbours, canals and bridges, and writing accounts of what he saw'.

Southwark Bridge was finished early in 1819 but it was not opened with the royal splendour that had surrounded the ceremony at Waterloo Bridge. The year was for Britain one of internal unrest and uncertainty. Agitation in regard to Parliamentary reform was to culminate in the dispersing of a meeting in Manchester by the military—the 'Peterloo' incident—and there was great concern about the state of George III, whose insanity (or more technically, acute intermittent porphyria) was to bring about his death in the following year. The Prince Regent did not feel that it was an appropriate time for regal display. Lord Dundas, Equerry to the Prince, wrote in a letter to the bridge company:

> The Prince has lately expressed some reluctance about such ceremonies, because he thinks he must go in State, and he has declined every invitation when it has been necessary for him to go in this manner, wishing not to make any ostentatious appearance in Public in the present situation of the King.

Also there was an additional reason why it was just as well for the bridge not to be opened with a very grand, and costly, ceremony. Not to put too fine a point on it, the Southwark Bridge Company had gone bust. At the simplest of ceremonies in March 1819 the bridge was officially declared open for public traffic by Sir John Jackson, chairman of the company, attended by the directors and a few friends. Then these company officials set about seeing what could be done for their creditors, among whom was Rennie.

In an article on iron bridges in the *Encyclopaedia Britannica*, Robert Stephenson wrote of the bridge that 'as an example of arch-construction, it stands confessedly unrivalled as regards its colossal proportions, its architectural effect, and the general simplicity of its details'. For a hundred years it did service and doubtless would still be there today were it not for the fact that, as with Rennie's Waterloo Bridge, the tremendous increase in motorized traffic in the 1920s demanded a much wider crossing of the river between Cannon Street in the City and Bridge Road in Southwark, and it was replaced by the present structure.

13 *London Bridge*

HISTORIANS seem to agree that the first mention of a London Bridge was in A.D. 43. In that year Aulus Plautius, Commander-in-Chief of the Roman army invading Britain, was pursuing a batch of Britons up country and made use of the bridge to press home the chase. Feeling among the historians is that it would have been 'a roughly built structure of Celtic workmanship'. But this was just an isolated mention of a bridge.

In 1832, just after Rennie's new London Bridge was completed, dredging was going on to deepen the channel and in the course of this many thousands of old Roman coins were brought up. These ranged in time from the consular period right up to Honorius, coins of the days of Nero, Lucilla, Sabina, Tacitus, Valerian. There were so many of them that it set the historians to fresh thought about Roman crossings of the Thames in the period when the settlement was Londinium. Perhaps there had been some sort of ritual, religious or otherwise, connected with tossing coins into the river from the bridge. This 'Three Coins in a Fountain' type theory sounded a bit thin. But so did the other possible explanation for all those coins on the bed of the Thames. Perhaps, said the antiquarians, the bridge mentioned may have been washed away and all crossing of the Thames at that point had been by ferrying. The coins reached the bottom of the river as people fell overboard when ferries capsized. Well. . . .

Communities do not usually establish themselves at a point on a river and then decide to build a bridge. It is more often the other way around. Clusters of people spring up around a river ford, ferry or bridge. R. E. M. Wheeler, writing in 1930, described London as 'a parasite of the Bridge'. But contemporary chroniclers in London's earliest days are most unhelpful as regards information about the settlement's bridge. Not until 963 was there another reference, and even that was oblique. It seems that in that year a widow and her son in the episcopate of Bishop

Aetholwold were found guilty of witchcraft and condemned to death by drowning. The *Codex Diplomaticus* reported:

> The district of Aegeleswyrthe had formerly condemned a widow and her son because they had driven pins into a figure of Aelsie Wulfstane's father, and they became detected and they drew that crime forth from the widow's chamber. Then they took that woman forth and drowned her at London Bridge and her son escaped and was outlawed.

It is not known exactly what sort of structure it was that the poor widow was lashed to at low tide to await her inevitable fate, but shortly after the year 1000 it is known definitely that London had 'a bridge of elm' built by the friars of the church established by one Mary Overs. How she came to endow the church on the south bank of the Thames is not without interest.

Mary Overs was the only daughter of a widower, John Overs, ferryman on the Thames. He had managed to obtain from the City authorities exclusive ferrying rights 'betwixt Southwark and the Churchyard Alley, being the high road way betwixt Middlesex, Surrey and London'. He was on to a good thing. He was making a fortune from his monopoly.

Mary was a girl of great beauty but she had no opportunity to make the fine match that her good looks would have ensured. Her father, to ward off fortune hunters, kept her under lock and key. However, a young man of Kent with more ingenuity than others keen to secure the wealth she would inherit was able on three occasions to have a secret meeting with Mary when father was at work at the ferry. The romance flourished so well that Mary decided she would marry her lover from Kent in defiance of her father. But it was then that things turned sour for poor Mary.

Her father gave no outward appearance of being a man of means. He was a miser with what today would be described as a pathological reluctance to spend any of his money. And it was this that brought about his downfall. In part payment of the meagre wages he paid those who worked for him he used to provide their meals, and one day there came to his warped mind what he felt was a wonderful idea to make a saving in food bills. His death would be announced and his staff would forthwith undertake a fast, which was the customary thing in those days at time of bereavement. He got Mary to sew him up in a sheet and the 'body' was laid out.

But far from his employees entering a period of fast, they saw this as a signal for rejoicing. They broke into his cellar and raided his larder. Not unnaturally, lying there in his sheet, Overs was furious at the sound of the merry-makers having their fill of his food and liquor. He decided to rise from the dead and give them a scare that they would never forget. But one of the men, flying right in the face of the fears of witchcraft prevalent at that time, grabbed the heavy part of a broken oar that was at hand and bashed it down on the sheet-draped ghost of John Overs. The miserly ferryman breathed his last.

When the news reached Mary's lover in Kent he was to horse and off like a flash, to get to London before anyone else could move in on Mary. But such was his eagerness to claim his bride that his horse, pushed to the limit, threw him and he broke his neck, fatally.

There was still more to come for the unfortunate Mary. In view of the circumstances of her father's death she could find no one who would give him Christian burial. It was only by delving into his reserves of cash and bribing the Friars of Bermondsey Abbey while the Abbot was away that she was able to have him interred in the sight of God. But when the Abbot returned he was horrified that his friars would do such a thing for gain. He ordered that the body be dug up again and taken out 'along Kent Street to the highway pond once called St Thomas a Waterings, common place of execution and burial ground of wrongdoers'.

All this was too much for Mary. She 'retired into cloisters', not however until she had made over her father's wealth to provide for the church which was to bear her name—the unhappily clinical-sounding St Mary Overies, on the site of what is now Southwark Cathedral.

The church became a 'college of Priests' and by 1136 they had completed the spanning of the Thames with a bridge made of sturdy elm. What became of this structure is not recorded. Fires in London being frequent, due in no small measure to the thatched roofs of the houses, it is possible that it burnt down. In any event, in 1176 Peter de Colechurch, one of the fraternity, decided that London should have a bridge of a more permanent character than could be created in wood.

This was considered outlandish for a variety of reasons. In the first place, timber was readily available in the heavily wooded areas adjoining the Thames but the nearest supply of stone suitable for building was some miles distant. It would be impossible to construct in the muddy bed of the river the secure foundations that would be needed to bear the weight of a stone bridge. The cost would be prohibitive. And, best reason of all not to use stone, wood had always been used before. But Peter 'the priest-builder' was a determined man. He argued that bridges of wood were in perpetual danger of being burnt. They were in constant need of repair, if not reconstruction, and the cost was always heavy. And finally, the growth of London demanded a more solid, a more imposing structure that would be a credit to the city.

He embarked on the project, eliciting the help of Henry II in financing it. The King levied a tax on wool, thus giving rise to the impression among the less bright citizens that the foundations were laid on woolpacks under the water. There were contributions also from the coffers of the Archbishop of Canterbury and the Papal Legate in England, Cardinal Hugocio di Petraleone.

For those looking back on Peter de Colechurch's tremendous achievement it is a matter of wonderment how he got the foundations down. It might have been thought that the river was turned, but as the Thames was tidal this would have been too vast an undertaking, requiring two huge barrages across the river. The construction of coffer dams for use in bridge building, developed by the Romans hundreds of years previously, had gone into abeyance. The manner of putting down the nineteen piers on which London's stone bridge was to stand might well have provided the origin for the expression 'doing it the hard way'. The foundations were laid right there in the flowing river. For each pier an enclosure was formed by driving in piles. The pile-driving 'engine' was on a barge, the weight being first raised, either by workers manhandling a capstan or by blindfold horses endlessly circling, and then tripped to crash down on the pile. Into the completed enclosure of piles was dumped loose rubble with chalk and gravel and upon this was built a wooden platform to take the masonry of the pier proper. Around each foundation was built a 'starling', a barricade pointed at each end to counteract the effect of the tidal flow of the river.

It was not surprising that the building of the foundations was to occupy most of the thirty-three years it took to construct the bridge, for as each new pier was built the more difficult it was to do the next. Since each pier with its starling was more than twenty feet in width, the bridge-builders were in effect building a weir across the Thames. As the total mass of the foundations was increased the flow of the river was further impeded and when working on the latter piers the men had to contend with water going like a mill race. More than two hundred and fifty lost their lives. Peter de Colechurch himself did not see the completion of the bridge. He died in 1205, after twenty-nine years of service to his project.

The bridge was 905 feet 10 inches in length, but the combined space occupied by the nineteen piers restricted the flow of the river to 503 feet. In time, rebuilding and extending of the starlings further impeded the flow, until the river had a mere 250 feet of freeway. Therefore, at such velocity did the water surge between the piers that going through by boat was called 'shooting the bridge'. The more timid travellers on the Thames would ask to be put ashore before reaching the bridge, to proceed on foot around it and rejoin their vessel on the other side—if it got through.

The bridge's road surface varied in width from twenty feet down to twelve feet, because of the encroachment of the houses, inns and shops built on either side. Traffic jams were a chronic condition. Pepys was to write of his carriage being held up for half an hour, at which he adjourned to a near-by inn, to find on emerging that it had been carried off in a sudden surge-through of the cluttered vehicles and he had to continue his journey on foot.

The cost of the upkeep of the bridge was offset partially by rent from the householders and shopkeepers as well as from toll charges. Toll bridges are always faced with the problem of how to collect the money without too much interruption of the flow of traffic. At London Bridge they had an ingenious scheme. Each bridge 'passenger' had to tender the correct amount for himself, vehicle, goods etc., otherwise he would be thrown into prison. The prison was handy—just by the south approach to the bridge, in Clink Street, which was of course the origin of the saying 'going to clink'.

Such was the affection Londoners had for their picturesque bridge that some left money in their wills. In 1300, for instance, Johanna Bytheweye left: 'To the work of London Bridge—twelve pence' and in 1301, Margery Bachelor bequeathed her gold wedding ring. But in the 1270s Eleanor, the Queen Mother, had shown another sort of affection for the bridge. She saw it as a wonderful source of personal revenue. She diverted to her own use the money collected from tolls. The bridge fell into a bad state of disrepair and it was only after a public outcry that the Wardens of the Bridge were to get such money put to its proper use.

Since, as mentioned, the bulk of the bridge's foundations made it a sort of weir the river upstream had the appearance of a placid lake and the still water had a tendency to freeze over when temperatures were down. In the winter of 1281 the pressure of the

ice on the foundations was so great that five arches gave way and
it took seven years to rebuild them. It was in this period that the
first of the many variations of the song 'London Bridge is Falling
Down' came into being.

At the parts of the bridge where there were no houses there
were chains at each side of the road surface to confine the con-
glomeration of wagons, carriages, pack horses, mules and travellers
on foot but they were not really adequate for the job and the
danger of toppling into the cataracts below was ever present.
In addition, especially at night, the bridge had its fair share of
London's footpads and other undesirable characters at the hands
of whom one could 'meet a death other than one's rightful death'.
Accordingly, at the approaches to the bridge groups of nuns were
on hand to give you, for a fee, their blessing for a safe passage
across.

Near the centre of the bridge was a chapel dedicated to St
Thomas à Becket and it was there that those on pilgrimage to
Canterbury to the scene of his martyrdom used to pause on their
journey for prayer. Peter de Colechurch died before the bridge
was finished, and his remains were transferred there, the only
burial on the bridge.

The first man to be involved in what was to become a gruesome
ritual on Old London Bridge was William Wallace of 'Scots wha
ha'e wi' Wallace bled' fame.

In 1304 Edward I, with the help of Bruce, had taken Stirling.
All the Northern Chieftains, with the exception of Wallace, had
submitted. He refused to surrender to the foreign foe, became an
outlaw and went into hiding. Promised that their banishment
would be curtailed if they found Wallace, the Northern Chiefs
hunted for him, to the disgust of many that 'men of the noblest
Scottish names stooped to pursue the hero'. He was captured on
4th August 1305, at Robroyston, near Glasgow, betrayed by Sir
John de Menteith, a Stewart and Sheriff of Dunbartonshire.

Wallace was brought to London and taken to a scaffold at one
end of Westminster Hall, where he was impeached as a traitor.
He pleaded that he could not be a traitor, since he had never
sworn allegiance to the English King. Found guilty, his sentence
was that 'his head be placed on London Bridge in sight of both
land and water travellers'. Before this was carried through, however, he was literally hanged, drawn and quartered. Having been
drawn at the tail of a horse through the streets of London, he was
hanged from a lofty gibbet, then taken down half dead. He was

disembowelled and then his head was cut off. His body was cut up into quarters which were to hang from gibbets in Newcastle, Berwick, Stirling and Perth.

The final stage of this gory business was completed when his head was set on a pole and set up above the drawbridge on London Bridge. One can understand with what sort of feeling a Wallace adherent, looking up at the head some time later, said: 'Alas that he was born!'

Kentishman Wat Tyler during the peasants' revolt of 1381 beheaded Simon of Sudbury, Archbishop of Canterbury, and placed his head on London Bridge with eight others, only for them to be taken down and replaced by his own head and that of Jack Straw, leader of the Essex rebels.

In 1535 when Sir Thomas More refused to acknowledge Henry VIII as supreme in the Church it was his fate to have his head erected on a pole on the bridge. It remained there for some time and it is said that one of his daughters, Margaret Roper, when passing under the bridge looked up at her father's head and said: 'That head has lain many a time in my lap. Would to God that it would fall into my lap as I pass under.' Her wish was granted, although not as dramatically as she indicated. Some months later when the head was removed from its pole to make room for another she was able to prevent it being thrown away into the river. She survived her father by only nine years and at her burial his head was indeed cradled in her lap.

With the executioners kept busy through to the time of the Stuarts, on London Bridge 'poles grew like a tropical forest'. The ghoulish ritual persisted until the beginning of the eighteenth century.

Despite the overcrowding in the two rows of houses and the *hautepas* linking the upper storeys of the houses above the roadway of the bridge, those who lived on Old London Bridge enjoyed much better health than those on shore. The simple reason for this was the absence of broken drains, open cesspits and noisome burial grounds—the common cause of disease and general ill-health among city-dwellers in the old days. Merely by opening their windows those who lived on the bridge had the benefit of cross-ventilation from the breeze that blows on the Thames, clearing the noxious air that normally hung over the city. They had no need of the nosegays and other devices for disguising smells essential for people to carry around even in their homes. Under their dwellings they had readily available a highly efficient sewage disposal system in the form of the fast flowing cataracts.

This of course was to give rise to the saying that London Bridge was for wise men to pass over and fools to pass under.

But apart from scoring high marks as far as clean air was concerned, noise was an ever present problem for the bridge dwellers. Thomas Pennant in *Some Account of London* wrote: 'They found it necessary to grow deaf to the noise of falling waters, the clamours of watermen and the frequent shrieks of drowning wretches.' In addition to the violent surge of water through the twenty arches of the bridge making it like living next door to a waterfall, those who were closest to the din of the waterwheels at the northern end felt as though they were perpetually on board a paddle steamer trying to make up time. Persons who for one reason or another moved from the bridge to live elsewhere found that it took some time to accustom themselves to getting to sleep at night in the strange quiet.

In the latter part of the seventeenth century many people made the move from the bridge to go and live in newly developed suburbs such as Islington, Hampstead and Chelsea. This started its slow decline as a place for families to live and, as a result, the general deterioration of the houses. It followed the familiar pattern to be observed in any big city: families living in a 'desirable residential district' move out when the growth of the city crowds in upon them or their homes become too old for practical upkeep, the big residences are turned into lodging houses, become more and more run down, and in due course have no other fate than to be pulled down for new development.

In the case of London Bridge it was not so much a matter of the residents feeling that the upkeep of the old house was too much of a burden. They were worried about falling into the Thames, house and all. The tidal river's constant pounding at the foundations had the houses 'overhanging and leaning in a terrific manner'. Tenants moved out to safer territory such as the heights of Hampstead. The landlords could charge only low rentals for life on the precarious bridge and lodgers, including a high percentage of rogues, whores and other shiftless characters, moved in. The going to seed of the residential area of London Bridge was well under way.

When Queen Anne came to the throne early in the eighteenth century 'the relic of the middle ages' built by Peter de Colechurch was still the only means of crossing the Thames at London apart from the boats of the watermen. But in 1738 work was started on a new bridge at Westminster and it was opened in the reign of George II in November 1749. The loss of revenue in tolls that this meant for the London Bridge authorities prompted them to decide that either they must modernize their bridge or replace it with an entirely new one. The City Surveyor submitted plans for a new bridge. The cost of £185,950 was deemed too high. The old one would be rebuilt and, bearing in mind the greatly increased wheeled traffic, the ramshackle, 'far from perpendicular' houses would be removed and the road surface thus considerably widened. An Act of Parliament sanctioning this work was passed on 25th January 1756 and demolition of the houses, shops and inns on the bridge began.

There was an immediate outcry. Members of the public bemoaned the fact that one of the most picturesque aspects of London was to go and all they would be left with would be a utilitarian bridge. The watermen were furious about all the business they would lose to the improved bridge.

The rebuilding included the removal of one of the piers and the construction of a 'great arch' near the centre, and while this was being undertaken a temporary wooden bridge was built across the span. Mysteriously this caught fire one night and was totally destroyed. It never was discovered how the fire started, but to ensure against a recurrence when a new one was put in its place there was a nightly patrol by 'a boat containing five men with blunderbusses and cutlasses'.

By 1762 all the houses were down and in the following year the rebuilding of Old London Bridge with its new naked look was complete. The improvement was of short-lived benefit. The modification which produced the great arch created a new problem. Water was drawn to that part of the bridge where it could flow with the greatest freedom and volume. The scouring action on the bed of the river under the wide arch put a strain on the piers at each side. Ballast from around and under the foundations was carried away. The structure there was weakened and adjoining arches were affected, meaning more patchwork, more repairs. The bridge was giving rise to as many if not more headaches now than before the building, since the problem has become the basic one of the foundations showing every sign of packing up completely after more than 550 years of service.

Things reached such a pass that in 1800 the Third Report from the Select Committee upon the Waterfront of the Port of London stated that there was nothing for it but to start again from scratch and build a brand new bridge. And as so often happens with such recommendations by special committees, years went by with no action taken.

In 1814 England's unpredictable climate decided to have a say

in the future of London Bridge. In February of that year a frost
descended upon the city the like of which had never been known
before. The coming and going of the tide built up the floes around
the foundations of the bridge until there was a stretch of solid ice
from bank to bank. This was a cause of annoyance to the watermen, for the good people of London were able to enjoy the novelty
of walking back and forth across the river, not only avoiding the
paying of bridge tolls but also not requiring a boat to get them
across. The efforts of watermen to extract a fee for the privilege of
crossing by means of pathways they had made with ashes thrown
on the ice were laughed to scorn. Londoners in fact were so keen
to enjoy this rarity of the Thames being frozen over that they
decided to hold a Frost Fair. Tents were erected on the ice, gay
flags were strung across, flares burned brightly by night. Whole
sheep roasted over a fire produced 'Lapland Mutton' at one
shilling a slice. Printing presses were set up to produce souvenir
copies of *Frostiana, Printed and Published on the Ice on the
River Thames*, containing such items as:

> You that walk here, and design to tell
> Your children's children what this year befell,
> Come buy this print and then it will be seen
> That such a year as this hath seldom been.

But although the great freeze-up was to provide Londoners
with a wonderful new conversation piece for many a year to
come, it did no good whatsoever for the foundations of London
Bridge. More repairs had to be effected to make good the ill effects
of the pack ice. Renewed urgings were made that the more con-
structive step of building an entirely new bridge must be taken.
As William Gifford, contemporary chronicler of the London scene
put it: 'This pernicious structure has wasted more money in
perpetual repairs than would have sufficed to build a dozen safe
and commodious bridges.'

The City of London authorities at last took action. Designs for
a new bridge were asked for, with the not very munificent
'premiums' of £250, £150 and £100 offered for the best three
received. More than a hundred designs were submitted, including
plans and models from such well-known architects and engineers
as Samuel Wyatt and Thomas Telford. One interesting plan, submitted by George Dance, Architect of the City and Professor of
Architecture at the Royal Academy, called for twin drawbridges
three hundred feet apart, with semicircles excavated out of each
bank to form a basin where shipping could be moored between

tides, so that traffic across the river would not be interrupted, one of the two drawbridges always being down.

A committee set up to pass judgment on these consisted of John Nash, the Nash of the terraces, John Soane, an eminent architect whose house in Lincoln's Inn Fields is now the Sir John Soane Museum, Robert Smirke and William Montague. At first the decision went in favour of the design submitted by Joseph Gwilt, F.S.A. Then it was changed and the main award went to Messrs William Fowler, T. Borer and Charles A. Busby. None of these in the end had anything to do with the design for the new London Bridge which was eventually decided upon.

The stature of John Rennie as a consulting engineer was by this time such that the Corporation of London had asked him to do a survey of the situation and he aproached this with his customary thoroughness. He studied the tides and currents. He had the river carefully sounded above and below the old bridge, from as high up as Teddington Lock down to the entrance of the London Docks. He examined the piers of the bridge down to their foundations and explored the bottom of the river, making borings at various points between one bank and the other. All this research was done to confirm that those who still felt that the ancient bridge could be saved, even if only in part, were quite wrong, and also to prepare the ground for designing an entirely new structure.

The 'visual' he drew up for his design is still to be seen in the library of the Institution of Civil Engineers in London. It is an impressive piece of artwork in full colour, measuring five feet ten inches by two feet two inches, folded into one of the two huge bound volumes entitled 'Collection of Drawings of Bridges and Other Engineering Works: John Rennie'.

The beautifully executed drawing of the plan and elevation of the five-arch link between Tooley Street on the north bank and St Magnus Church on the south is headed: 'DESIGN of A BRIDGE proposed to be erected over the RIVER THAMES instead of the present LONDON BRIDGE, by John Rennie, 1821.' For the technically minded there is the reference:

Middle Arch	150 ft span	29.6 above Trinity High Water Mark
Second Arches	140 ft	do. each
Third Arches	130 ft	do. each
Middle Piers	24 ft	
Side Piers	22 ft	
Roadway	45 ft in the clear	

Cost of Bridge and Aproaches, deducting the property removed £.

It was this design which he included in his report to the City Corporation delivered on 12th March 1821 and they in turn included it in their application to Parliament in the same year for 'An Act for the Rebuilding of London Bridge and for the Improving of and making suitable Approaches Thereto'. Rennie was to die, in June 1821, without knowing the result of the deliberations in Parliament about his bridge. Opposition to the Bill in both Houses by those who felt that there was no necessity for a new bridge and that its erection would only be a waste of money delayed its passage by two years. But by then a Committee of the House of Commons, having examined the Rennie design and those submitted to the competition, proposed that his be finally adopted. On 4th July 1824 the Bill received Royal Assent, with the younger John Rennie empowered to carry his father's plan into effect.

The building of a new London Bridge being regarded as of national importance, £150,000 towards the cost was allocated from the National Exchequer, the remainder to be raised on credit by the Bridge House Estates, recipients of the revenues from the old bridge.

The first pile was driven on 15th March 1824, a hundred feet up river from the old bridge. By the middle of the following year the first coffer dam had been constructed and on the tenth anniversary of the battle of Waterloo the foundation stone was laid inside the dam, which had been impressively covered over by a huge marquee festooned with flags. *The Times* reported:

The first stone of the grand national undertaking was laid on 15th June, 1825, by the Lord Mayor [Garratt], accompanied by H.R.H. the Duke of York and others. The coffer-dam on that occasion presented one of the most extraordinary appearances that such a construction ever exhibited. . . . When seated at the bottom of the capacious structure formed in the midst of the roaring waters of that part of the Thames, no one would have believed, from the appearances around the crowded recesses of the dam, while they were pacing the crimson carpeting that covered the temporary boarded floor, and surveying the beautiful mass of granite that was suspended as the first stone of the bridge, that they were then treading the newly explored bed of old Father Thames and were nearly five and forty feet below the high water mark of the mighty current that was divided to the right and left like a wall, and rushing by and above them.

There was a contretemps when the Lord Mayor and the Duke of York could not decide who should occupy the Chair of State, so it stayed empty as they remained standing each side of it throughout the ceremony—less of a hardship for the Duke, wearing merely the plain blue coat and knee-breeches of the Order of the Garter, while the Lord Mayor was weighed down by his furred robes of scarlet and the massive chain of office over his shoulders.

The inscription on the brass plate on the foundation stone was composed by the Rev. Edward Copplestone, D.D., Master of Oriel College, Oxford, and it read:

> The free course of the river being obstructed by the numerous piers of the ancient bridge, and the passage of boats and vessels through its many channels being often attended with danger and loss of life by reason of the force and rapidity of the current, the City of London, desirous of providing a remedy for this evil and at the same time consulting the convenience of commerce in this vast emporium of all nations, with the sanction and with the liberal aid of Parliament, resolved to erect a new bridge upon a foundation altogether new, wth arches of wider span, and of a character compatible to the dignity and importance of this royal city: nor does any other time seem more suitable for such an undertaking than when, in a period of universal peace, the British Empire flourishing in glory, wealth, population and domestic unison, is governed by a prince, the patron and encourager of the arts, under whose auspices the metropolis had been daily advancing in elegance and splendour.

> The first stone of this work was laid by the Right Hon[ble] John Garratt, Lord Mayor of London, on the 15th day of June, in the sixth year of King George IV and in the year 1825.

> John Rennie, F.R.S. Architect.

The ceremony conducted more than forty feet below the surface of the river went off without mishap but shortly afterwards son John Rennie was to meet with an accident there. In his own words:

> After this pier had advanced nearly to the level of high water, one day whilst examining it, standing upon one of the cross beams, my foot slipped, and I fell headlong into the dam upon the top of the masonry; fortunately, my left foot had caught in a nail on the beam, and I hung by it for a few seconds. This

Opening of Rennie's Bridge 1831

Radio Times Hulton Picture Library

Old London Bridge

New London Bridge

Demolishing and rebuilding being done simultaneously

Work on the new bridge progresses

somewhat broke and changed the direction of my fall, and I pitched upon an inclined plank, upon which I slid until I struck my head against a stone; my hat deadened the blow; as it was, however, I was cut about the forehead and half stunned. The after effects of this fall were very serious; my whole system got such a shaking, that I did not recover thoroughly until nearly ten years afterwards, and I carried on my large professional business with the greatest difficulty.

However, he was able to report that 'the works made satisfactory progress' on the bridge his father had specified 'must be built of the best grey granite' brought from Aberdeen, Devon and Cornwall, with the masonry below low water composed of hard sandstone grit from Bramley Fall, near Leeds—a total weight of stonework which was eventually to reach 130,000 tons.

He was thankful for continued support from Whitehall and wrote of it in these terms:

Lord Liverpool's Government had always taken the greatest interest in the construction of new London Bridge, and gave the Corporation of London every support in their power, not only for the accommodation of the great traffic across it, but for the improvement of the Thames, which the removal of the old bridge would effect. . . . That amiable, able and conscientious nobleman, the Earl of Liverpool, had succumbed to the effects of a paralytic stroke [1828] and the Duke of Wellington was now Premier; he took the greatest interest in the promotion of London Bridge and everything connected with it; so that the Corporation of London, who had hitherto been radically inclined, or had rather been opposed to the Tory Government, turned rather Conservative than otherwise, and the Duke became most popular with them; he invariably, whenever he could accepted their invitations to Guildhall and the Mansion House, and was always received by them with the greatest respect and attention. Richard Lambert Jones, the Chairman of the London Bridge Committee was his particular favourite, and he always shook Jones by the hand, a favour which he did not accord to everyone.

The Duke of Wellington's personal interest was a great help when, in January 1829, the fifth and final arch was spanned and with completion of the bridge in sight it was necessary to turn to the complicated and far more costly aspect of the approaches. Roads to be diverted, viaducts to be constructed, rebuilding of streets adjoining the bridge on both sides of the Thames—it was a vast project with an estimated cost of £1,400,000. Where was the money to come from?

The Duke of Wellington took the greatest interest in the subject, and investigated it to the fullest extent; he visited the place himself, he interrogated the Chairman of the Bridge Committee and myself most closely, and at length, being fully convinced that it was necessary, gave the consent of the Government, provided that the funds could be found. In order to meet this difficulty it was proposed to increase the coal tax.

Early in 1829 a Bill was brought into Parliament, and was most strongly opposed by the great northern coal-owners, Lord Durham, Lord Londonderry, Lord Lauderdale and others. After a hard fight the Bill passed the House of Commons and got into the Lords; but here the opposition was more violent and powerful than ever. The Duke of Wellington, however, having been thoroughly convinced of the necessity and justice of the measure, determined that it should be carried if possible, whilst the Opposition were equally determined to throw it out. The Committee accordingly met in the Painted Chamber of the House of Lords, and the extraordinary number of forty peers, including seven cabinet ministers, assembled, the Duke of Wellington being in the chair. Such a committee upon a private Bill has never since been seen in the Lords, and perhaps never will be again. The brunt of the battle fell upon me; I was the leading witness, and had to establish the whole case. I never felt more nervous in my whole life.

He survived the ordeal and the Duke was able to get the Bill through. The work on the approaches proceeded. In Parliament, however, there were changes.

In 1830 the Duke's Government retired, and he himself became as unpopular as he before had been popular; yet he never deserted London Bridge, and was more frequent in his visits than ever. I often used to attend him at five and six in the summer mornings; he generally came on horseback, and remained from half an hour to an hour, and sometimes more if necessary.

The bridge and its approaches were finished by the end of July 1831, seven years and four months from the driving of the first pile. As mentioned earlier Rennie, in the specifications of his original design, had left the estimated cost blank. The money expended for the entire operation turned out to be as follows:

Cost of new structure and construction of land
   arches   £680,232
Approaches and alterations to a number of streets   £1,840,438
Demolition of Old Bridge   £35,500
                         Total   £2,556,170

It is interesting to note that the approaches cost almost three
times as much as the bridge itself. The cost in lives: of the eight
hundred men employed on the project, forty were killed or
drowned.

The opening of the new London Bridge by King William IV and
Queen Adelaide on 1st August 1831 was described by John Rennie
the younger as 'perhaps, as a spectacle of the kind, the most
brilliant of any that had taken place for fully a century'.

The Times devoted no less than four and a half columns of its
customary four-page issue (price 7*d*.) to the report of the event, of
which the main feature was the Royal progress from the Palace to
Somerset House and thence by barge to the huge tented pavilion
erected at the north end of the bridge and bedecked with 'flags,
shields and standards of armies that had formerly waved over the
armies of almost every civilised country in the world'.

The atmosphere of the occasion was recorded by *The Times* in
this manner:

    The Royal Family and their Majesties' suite assembled at the
Palace at about 2 o'clock and at a quarter before 3 o'clock
the Royal procession, consisting of 12 carriages, was formed in
the garden of the Palace. An escort composed of the Life and
Royal Horse Guards was in attendance. The Royal Cavalcade
passed up the east side of the Palace, through the iron gates
by Marlborough House into Pall Mall, on their way to Somerset House.

    The appearance of the metropolis along the whole line
through which the procession passed was in one respect as if it
were a kept holyday. The shops were closed, and business
seemed altogether suspended. In every place the streets were
crowded with a dense mass, which loudly cheered the Royal
Party in its progress.

    Raising of the Royal standard at Somerset House, to signal
arrival of the procession, was greeted with loud huzzas from
the crowds on the water and at both sides and was followed
by discharges of cannon of all sorts from the wharves and
barges.

    The scene at this moment was inexpressively grand. Her
Majesty repeatedly bowed and the King was frequently

uncovered in acknowledgment of these marks of devotion and affectionate attachment.

Houses, wharfs and warehouses which abutted the river were filled with spectators from 12 o'clock, and they were entertained by military bands, by the German minstrels, by the celebrated Siffleur, and by that still more celebrated performer, who has demonstrated his independence of all musical instrument makes by playing tunes upon his chin with his fists.

In the Royal Procession was Sir Robert Peel and his lady. The right hon. baronet who had opposed the first Reform Bill was extremely ill-received by some of the company who gave a tolerably intelligible opinion of his late conduct by hissing him.

A barge with a military band and 21 brass cannon continued to fire at intervals and at the conclusion of the ceremony proper, in going to and returning from the Surrey end of the bridge, their Majesties threw medals to the spectators on either side of them.

Having watched 'a balloon ascension by the two aeronauts Mr Green and Mr Crawshay', the Royal party sat down to a cold collation washed down with what were described as extremely good wines at 'a banquet that was conducted on a scale of profuseness that was remarkable even in civic feasts'. At 6 o'clock their Majesties rose to leave and 'thus concluded one of the most gorgeous festivals in the annals of the metropolis'.

The Times of those days was not entirely objective in its news reporting. Although this was an account of the opening of the bridge the paper could not resist the temptation to pass comment on the state of royalty in Britain. William IV, who had just come to the throne in the previous year, was highly commended by the paper for his obvious desire to get out and about among his subjects, something which was very much appreciated by them. It was in striking contrast to his predecessor, George IV, of whom *The Times* said: 'A king who travels in a closed carriage with lightning's speed and whose arrival is announced only by half a dozen lancers cannot expect that his subjects will care very much about him personally.'

When the new bridge was in full use by the public much of the old bridge still remained and demolition was not complete until several years later. Gordon Home, author of *Old London Bridge*, published in 1931, expressed himself unhappy about one aspect of the demolition. He wrote that when the wreckers reached the floor of the lower chapel where the remains of Peter de Colechurch were:

Londoners ready enough to do honour to the designer of their new bridge destroyed, without giving more than the briefest newspaper paragraphs to record the event, the resting place and the remains of the pioneer of European fame who first designed a great bridge of stone in the British Isles.

That author was also pained at what little interest there was in retaining parts of the old bridge as a monument. He listed various places where portions of the original structure were still to be seen. Some of the stone was used in building a dwarf wall in front of houses No. 47 to 73 in Heathfield Road near Wandsworth Common. There was other stone at the entrance to a mews in Ennismore Gardens on the south of Hyde Park. Stone refuges from the bridge were in the courtyard of Guy's Hospital and in Victoria Park in the East End of London. Iron railings were to be seen in Bishopsgate by the side of the footpath through the churchyard opposite the school.

In 1921, however, a wonderful opportunity to preserve a whole arch of Old London Bridge, *in situ,* was missed. When the Pearl Insurance Company's old building between the Church of St Magnus and Rennie's bridge was being pulled down to make way for Adelaide House the second arch from the north of Old London Bridge was revealed under the foundations. It was suggested that this be incorporated into the new building as a memorial. But it was pointed out that changing the plans would cost £7,000. Despite the efforts of author Gordon Home and others, the money could not be raised.

Sir Malcolm McAlpine started a scheme to re-erect the arch at the British Empire Exhibition at Wembley. But the stones crumbled when disturbed and now all that can be seen of the arch by the public is some of the stonework on the roof garden of Adelaide House and in front of the tower of St Magnus-the-Martyr on what used to be the roadway of Old London Bridge.

Rennie's London Bridge was to have a much happier fate.

14 *The Newest London Bridge*

'RENNIE built for posterity', wrote Samuel Smiles. This certainly applies in the case of Kelso Bridge, still as firm as a rock more than a century and a half later, and others of his bridges in Britain's hinterland. In such places as Musselburgh and Stewart Newton, where nothing much has happened since 1880, a venerable stone bridge has a good chance of indefinite survival. In London, however, with its persistent increase in population and corresponding increase in traffic, a Rennie bridge was naturally put to much more of a test.

In 1902, to meet the demands of twentieth-century traffic, his London Bridge was widened from its original fifty-six to sixty-nine feet. This allowed for a conversion from two to four lanes on the carriageway and in this way the bridge was to be granted a longer life than his Waterloo Bridge, where increase in width had not been deemed practical.

In effect, however, it was merely a reprieve. By the beginning of the 1960s it was felt that London Bridge must not only have six lanes to cope with the city's share of the ten million vehicles that by then had come on to the roads but also wider footpaths to accommodate the increasing flood of train commuters going back and forth from London Bridge Station over on the south side of the river. A survey revealed that during the morning and evening 'rush', more than twenty thousand people on foot and just short of three thousand vehicles were crossing the bridge each hour. Engineers made a study of the Rennie structure with a view to further widening. It was known that within a year of its opening 130 years previously there had been an uneven settlement which had given the bridge a noticeable downstream tilt, but a commissioner of engineers of that time which had included the great Thomas Telford had pronounced it perfectly safe, a verdict that had remained true over the years. The modern engineers, however, decided that to put additional top hamper on the original foundations was not feasible. A new bridge should be built in its place.

Accordingly the Corporation of the City of London sought Parliamentary consent to the rebuilding and this was eventually granted with the passing of the London Bridge Act 1967. The City Engineer, Harold K. King, C.B.E., C.Eng., F.I.C.E., F.I.Mun.E., F.R.I.C.S., then swung into action despite the encumbrance of all those initials and in October 1967 contracts were assigned to: Mott, Hay and Anderson, consulting engineers responsible for the design and site supervision of the work; William Holford and Partners, who were retained to advise on architectural treatment of the new bridge; and John Mowlem and Company Limited, contractors for the demolishing of the old and the building of the new, based on a successful tender of £4,066,000.

No time was lost in starting work. Demolition of the old bridge commenced on 7th November 1967. Although more than five months were to elapse during which various announcements were made about the effort, eventually successful, to sell Rennie's bridge the contractors had known when they started pulling it down that it had been sold. They had to know. Taking a bridge down to re-erect it elsewhere is naturally a quite different operation from just bashing it down to get it out of the way for new development.

In setting out to sell Rennie's bridge as an entity rather than breaking it up and disposing of it for the value of the stone (as with his Waterloo Bridge), the City Corporation were at pains to ensure that at its new site, wherever that might be, it would not be degraded by being converted to house a fun fair or some such thing.

In *The Times* of 12th March 1968 there was a story datelined New York which stated that 'Ivan Luckin, member of the City of London Common Council, here to sell London Bridge, said America would be a fitting place for it because it had been an inspiration to Englishmen who settled in the new world. This was a bit of hokum, salesmanship of the type which might be calculated to appeal to Americans. One would have to question a great number of English migrants in the United States before encountering one who was likely to say that thinking about London Bridge carried him through his darkest hours in his new country.

The fact of the matter is that not all Londoners, let alone Englishmen in general, have ever seen London Bridge. It is purely a matter of geography. Since it is down in the City, it is only seen regularly by those who work in London's financial district or have cause to go there. Commuters who live in the south-east tip of England use it each day coming and going from the London Bridge main-line station. But there are a vast number of Londoners who never have any reason to go to that part of the city.

When it was decided in 1967 to sell Rennie's London Bridge, the Corporation of London produced a splendid prospectus, which has now become a collector's item. Designed by Anthony Smith and Roger Turpin and printed by the WLP Printing Group, it is a beautifully produced sixteen-page booklet with coil binding, a variety of well-chosen printing papers and pull-out 'gatefold' illustrations in full colour which are themselves worth framing. It traces the history of London Bridge from Roman times to today, with contemporary drawings, engravings and photographs and reproductions of documents relating to the bridge. On the inside cover even the music and lyrics of *London Bridge is Falling Down* are there for anyone who would care to dash it off on the piano.

It is a lush, expensive production and the undisclosed cost of distributing thousands of copies throughout the world must have been high. But after all it was bait for what the Corporation hoped would be bids of more than a million pounds and as such was not extravagant. The practical side of the prospectus comes at the end, where there are detailed architectural drawings of what was actually for sale and a Form of Tender for prospective buyers to fill in with the instructions: 'Tenders must be enclosed in the attached envelope, sealed and addressed to The Town Clerk, Corporation of London . . . on or before noon on the 29th day of March 1968.'

Bids came in from all over the world—the United States, Canada, Switzerland, Spain, France and Korea. The form of tender filled in by the president of McCulloch Oil Corporation at their head office in Los Angeles was for $2,460,000 (something over £1 million). They proposed to make it the centrepiece of a new city they were building on Lake Havasu in Arizona and as it seemed an estimable function for Rennie's bridge and the price was good, their bid was accepted.

Thrilled at their purchase, the buyers announced that 'if things go the way they are expected, the bridge will become Arizona's biggest attraction since the creation of the Grand Canyon'.

There is no truth whatsoever in the rumour that the purchasers were under the impression that they were buying Tower Bridge, which so many people all over the world are convinced is called London Bridge, and that they were terribly disappointed when what they got was not that colourful bridge which opens up for tall ships to pass. However, it is a certainty that when Rennie's London Bridge is opened at Lake Havasu City more than a few tourists who go there to see it are going to feel let down.

Lake Havasu City, designed as 'a resort, light industry and retirement community', is about a hundred and fifty miles from the Grand Canyon and ninety miles below the famous Hoover Dam on a part of the Colorado River that became an extensive lake with the building of the Parker Dam some fifty miles downstream.

During the war the U.S. Government built an auxiliary airfield along the shore and the isolated location, then known merely as Site Six, became a rest and recuperation centre for servicemen. After the war when the military had departed it became what was described as a 'a fisherman's secret paradise'. In 1962 the Government gave the 12,900 acres of Site Six to Arizona who sold it to McCulloch Properties Inc., a wholly-owned subsidiary of the McCulloch Oil Corporation, for $954,329. A community of some 400 residents, it was expected within twenty years to be a complete city of 100,000 after an eventual investment of more than £7,000 millions.

The inspiration behind the purchase and transporting of London Bridge to Lake Havasu was the success of Disneyland. The McCulloch organization did a great deal of research into the significance of that mecca of tourists before embarking on their Arizona project. In an announcement, they said:

The fact that Lake Havasu has nearly 8,000,000 people annually travelling the major interstate highways to the north and south means that millions of visitors can be attracted to a masterfully executed International Resort Area which will have as its centrepiece the legendary London Bridge. To analyse some of the potential involved, the following is a review of the impact of a major commercial recreation project on the once relatively small community of Anaheim, Calif., site of Disneyland.

In 1954, Anaheim had a population of 23,000. Twelve years later it had grown to nearly 160,000, an increase of almost 600 per cent. In 1954 Anaheim's taxable retail sales amounted to $37,056,000. By the end of 1966 Anaheim had recorded $335,664,000 in taxable retail sales, a jump of over 800 per cent. Even more spectacular in this same interval was the sky rocketing of land values of all classes—residential lots, subdivision acreage, commercial and industrial parcels. Property rose from 350 to 1,700 per cent in value.

The meteoric figures sound like the work of a magician—and, to a great extent, they were. The magician was the immortal Walt Disney; his wand, Disneyland, and his gift to Anaheim the priceless commodity of millions of tourists. Now [1968] in the thirteenth season, Disneyland has become a mecca for pleasure-seekers the world over, its very name a synonym for imagination and escape. But to the analytical minds of professional economists, Disneyland represents something else —a new form of financial phenomenon they designate as a 'recreation industry generator'.

One highly respected team of analysts which had been prominent in studies of commercial recreation projects is Economic Research Associates of Los Angeles, Calif. . . . It was in its 1964 report on the impact of 10 years of Disneyland that the ERA firmly enunciated its concept of the 'recreation industry generator' phenomenon. Referring to its Disneyland and similar surveys ERA noted that 'the conclusion drawn is that this class of business, drawing from a wide region outside its site, has a greater economic velocity and multiplier effect on its environment than any other known industry'. . . . Calling Disneyland's 10-year impact on Anaheim 'spectacular' —an unusual adjective in an economic report—ERA said that 'in 10 years the catalytic, self-generating economic effect of recreation associated with Disneyland has brought well over one-half billion dollars into the economy of Anaheim. . . .

In 1955 there was but one motel in the Disneyland area—in 1968, fifty motels and five hotels. . . . In 1965 the Los Angeles baseball club built a $21,000,000 stadium and moved there lock, stock and ball club. . . . In 1967 the city built a $15,000,000 Convention Center, a multi-purpose arena. . . . In 1955 the city boasted 105 industries and during 1967 this climbed to 460 industries . . .

Not unnaturally the local authorities were very happy about Anaheim's 'growth potential' thanks to Disneyland, 'the recreation industry generator', and the McCulloch organization punched this home with the tailpiece:

But perhaps the best example of Anaheim's regard for Disneyland comes from a city official who said: 'Every once in a while I have a nightmare in which I relive those early days when Walt Disney was pondering about where to locate Disneyland. In my nightmare he decides on San Francisco and I wake up with an almost uncontrollable urge to drive over and see if Disneyland is still here. I know it will be, but if it weren't I think I would just keep on driving.'

Any visionary in the construction business could not help but be inspired by the example of Disneyland. Such a man was Robert P. McCulloch, president of the McCulloch Corporation, 'described by associates as a "diversified genius"—engineer, designer and business administrator with a flair for finance, planning and showmanship'. As an indication of just how diversified his genius is his corporation is 'one of the world's largest manufacturers of chain saws and outboard motors'.

It seems that in the late 1950s McCulloch made a prolonged aerial search of the western part of the States for an inland body of water that would be suitable for establishing an outboard-motor test centre. When he flew over Havasu he observed the broad blue expanse of water (*ha-va-su* is Indian for 'blue water'), the gently sloping Arizona shoreline and the airport peninsula that juts out into the lake. This was where he would build a new city.

His dream was realized when in 1964 he bought the twenty-six square miles of lake-front property and assigned to C. V. Wood Jnr, president of the McCulloch Oil Corporation, the task of creating the master plan for the city-to-be.

By happy coincidence Wood was also an engineer, designer and business administrator with a flair for finance, planning and showmanship.

They poured all these skills into Lake Havasu City, resolving to make it a 'complete city' with an economy based on light industry and recreation enterprises.

Lake Havasu City, a master-planned community, is now faced with the potential of a burgeoning new industry——'leisure industry' now foresees a local economy based on one-third general recreation—light industrial employment, one-third recreation-leisure 'industry' and one-third commercial-service employment. This is planned to give dynamic balance to growth to the City.

'What we needed,' says Wood, 'was a centrepiece for our leisure industry, a great drawing attraction for travellers and vacationers that would persuade them to turn off the major transcontinental highways to the north and south and drive into Lake Havasu City.'

The centrepiece and great drawing attraction—232 air miles east of Los Angeles, 150 air miles northwest of Phoenix, 135 air miles south of Las Vegas and approximately 7,000 air miles west of Piccadilly Circus—will be London Bridge—an old veteran learning new tricks.[1]

[1] *Lake Havasu City Herald*, May 1968.

Meanwhile, back in London the dismantling of Rennie's bridge and the work on the new one was well under way.

Designing a new bridge over the Thames has never been a simple matter, taking into account all the problems caused by the tidal nature of the river, the difficulties of getting adequate approaches through the congestion of buildings on either bank, the allowances that have to be made for river navigation and so on. But the planning of this new London Bridge was made especially difficult by the fact that the designers were not starting from scratch. The new bridge had to occupy the same site as the old. The trick they had to perform was to keep the vehicular and pedestrian traffic flowing while demolishing the old bridge and building the new one over the top of it. The basic design was directly related to overcoming this problem.

Although the bridge has three arches it is not in the strict sense an arch bridge, like Rennie's. In the case of Rennie's bridge it was the five stone arches that held up the bridge. The rôle of the arches in the modern structure is merely to give secondary support. Technically speaking, it has been designed as 'four parallel pre-stressed concrete box beams—each in itself a complete bridge'.

The best way to understand this is to place two blocks flat on a table a few inches apart, to represent the banks of the Thames, and across the gap place four pencils side-by-side. These are the four concrete box beams. In the actual bridge they are supported by two piers in the river that divide the bridge into three spans and the arches of these three spans give additional support. Now —look at these pencils, the four box beams stretching right across the river. Here's the clever bit. The two outside ones are the footpaths on each side of the bridge; the two in the centre are the two halves of the roadway, three lanes going one way and three the other way.

Demolishing and building at the same time, the traffic was kept flowing by first completing the footpath on the upstream (west) side and diverting all the road traffic on to that. Pedestrians were channelled on to the middle, old roadway while they went to work on the other footpath. This downstream (east) footpath was the first part of the bridge to be brought to its final form and it was officially opened on 22nd February 1971.

With pedestrians thus catered for on a completed footpath and motor traffic temporarily using the other, they were able to go to work on the two middle box beams, which combined would provide six lanes for vehicles. By stages they could divert the motor traffic from its temporary route along the first footpath and complete that for pedestrian use. By this leap-frogging technique London Bridge was kept in use throughout the transition from old to new and it was expected that the whole operation would be completed by mid-1972.

An interesting thing to notice when crossing the new London Bridge on foot is that the pavement you are walking on is not flat. Naturally it slopes slightly towards the curb for rain water to drain off but apart from that it has a convex curve, bulges upwards in other words. If it didn't, it would look as though it sagged in the middle. In architecture it is a common optical illusion that something that is straight, like the top of a wide window or a broad pavement, appears to sag and to counteract this designers use 'entasis', which our dictionary tells us is the introduction of convexity to correct the visual illusion of concavity.

The footpath on the downstream (east) side completed and opened to the public in February 1971 is twenty-one feet in width—six feet wider than the footpath on the other side. Why this rare lop-sided design? The explanation is simply that London Bridge railway terminus, one of London's busiest commuter stations, is at the south-eastern approach to the bridge. Each morning it spills out—and each evening draws in—a flood of humanity from the eastern part of Surrey, West Sussex and Kent. These people work in the City. The shortest route on foot between the station and their work is by way of the downstream footpath of London Bridge—there is no reason to risk one's neck crossing the traffic on the bridge to use the other footpath. Since London Bridge Station was opened in Victorian times (a safe statement to make, since no London main-line station has been built this century), it has always been that way, and in any old photographs of traffic on Rennie's London Bridge it will be observed that the downstream footpath is crowded and the other one relatively deserted.

Looking at the newest London Bridge in profile one is at once struck by how thin the arches and piers are in comparison to the bulkiness of Rennie's bridge. It is not necessarily more attractive. Even the layman detects that the ends of the two shore arches just seem to 'sit' on each bank of the river. They neither blend into the shoreline nor complete the arch to make the bridge an entity in itself, as with Rennie's admirable design. It gives the appearance that there was a miscalculation, that the new bridge was too long and a bit had to be chopped off each end to make it fit the width of the river.

A simple way to understand what pre-stressing means is to

think what can happen when you lift a dozen books, say, from a shelf. With pressure exerted inwards by each of your hands, the row of boks can be held out in front of you. However, if someone presses a hand down on them, they will collapse—unless you squeeze harder. The more firmly you press them together, the more weight will the row of books withstand. Technically they are in tension. Now take this priciple over into reinforced concrete. The steel wires or rods inside a slab of concrete are stretched either before or after the concrete is set. Naturally they want to return to their former, shorter length when released from the stretching mechanism and this pulling-in of the concrete puts it in tension in just the same way as your hands pressing on the books. This method of strengthening concrete and making it capable of withstanding much more weight was first patented by P. H. Jackson of San Francisco, in 1888. But its practical application was not entirely successful and it was not until 1928 that the French engineer Eugène Freyssinet perfected the process. It began to be extensively used on the Continent and in Britain in the 1940s, was first used in America on a bridge in Philadelphia and has now been universally adopted for wide, graceful spans that are 'wafer thin' compared to the bulk of masonry or concrete needed in the past. As mentioned earlier, pre-stressed concrete has come into its own particularly for use in the freeways, fly-overs and clover-leafs seen to be cropping up on the motorways all over the countryside.

An interesting aspect of the design of the modern London Bridge is that it will incorporate what the builders call 'a Rennie museum'. In other words they will do properly what Herbert Morrison's LCC did in a half-hearted way when they rebuilt Rennie's Waterloo Bridge. Visitors to the new London Bridge will be able to walk down under the first arch on the north bank and gain an impression of what it was like on Rennie's bridge, from part of the original abutment left *in situ* and four of the old lamp standards on a portion of the original balustrading, plus other fixtures and data about the 1831 bridge.

This new London Bridge is perhaps unique in regard to its financing. Normally any bridge on this scale would place demands on local ratepayers and the National Exchequer, just as the new Waterloo Bridge was financed from rates and Government grants. The modern London Bridge, however, has made no such call on the taxpayer. It is being paid for from funds of the Bridge House Estates plus the proceeds from the sale of Rennie's bridge.

The Bridge House Estates we encountered earlier when dealing with Old London Bridge. It is the body that was set up originally by the City Corporation for the collection of tolls and the rental of properties on Old London Bridge. During the six hundred years and more of that bridge's existence a tidy sum was amassed, augmented by shrewd investment. Deducting the more than £1 million which McCulloch Properties paid for Rennie's bridge, the Bridge House Estates were still left with over £3½ millions to find, but such are their resources that they have been able to take that formidable figure in their stride.

As soon as the news went around the world that London Bridge was coming down letters poured in to the City Corporation with requests for bits as souvenirs. An application with a two-dollar bill enclosed, from a young boy named Roderick Todd, of Victoria, British Columbia, was the first received. The contractors sent him a piece and returned the money with their compliments.

During the work of demolishing the old and building the new bridge special care had to be exercised in regard to shipping passing underneath. Oxy-acetylene welding, pneumatic drills sending off sparks from the granite—there was great danger from these if an oil tanker happened to be passing. Bits of masonry falling into the river could be a hazard, especially to the sight-seeing boats with open decks packed with tourists, since the operators of these boats inclined to loiter around the bridge to give their customers a good look at what was going on. But these worries were soon put to an end. A chunk of stone dropped onto the bridge of a passing ship, falling right at the feet of the skipper. The blast he let off then was repeated more formally to the authorities and it was arranged that from then on there would be a look-out who would warn of approaching vessels by ringing a bell and work would be halted until they had passed through. During the latter, more extensive operations at the bridge site there was a system of traffic lights on the arches to control the navigation and keep interruptions to the work down to a minimum.

As a further safety measure the contractors employed John McGrath, of East Ham, to patrol the Thames in a powered rubber dinghy of the type used in navy air-sea rescue in case any of the workmen on the bridge should fall into the river. None did, but he saved the lives of two other people who fell in.

A census of shipping passing under London Bridge was taken for a month starting from September 1970 and it was found that there was an average of 319 vessels a day. Anyone hearing this figure will immediately say that it does not sound like very many.

And this is quite true. The fact of the matter is that river traffic on the Thames at central London is dwindling rapidly. Within six months of the census the figure had dropped dramatically and it was predicted that we would not be far into the 1970s before practically the only vessels to be seen on the river above Tower Bridge would be pleasure craft.

A basic reason for this, as described in the chapter on Rennie's London docks, has been the change in cargo-handling methods whereby commodities are brought into London in larger units which only the bigger docks down river are now capable of handling. Today it is very rare to see the coastal and Continental freighters and the barges and the tankers that used to put in at the little wharves on the banks of the Thames as high up the river as Waterloo Bridge. One by one the wharves are closing, going derelict from loss of business. Not a fish has been put ashore at Billingsgate Market, on the river adjoining London Bridge, in the 1970s so far. There is now no reason whatsoever for the fishmarket to be at that location. As with the Covent Garden fruit and vegetable market it could be moved elsewhere to make valuable property available for redevelopment. Only the veterans, clinging to its centuries-old traditions, are fighting for its survival.

Normally it is a matter of regret to see the dwindling of what was a thriving trade, as was the wharfage along this part of the Thames, but in this case it is, in the long term, one of the best things that could have happened to London. Always it has been a cliché to say how terrible the banks of the Thames in the heart of London look in comparison to the Seine in Paris. Being a hundred miles inland, where the Seine was not an industrial river, Paris had the advantage of being able to beautify its banks. All that could be done for Londoners was the building in the 1860s of the Victoria Embankment and in more modern times across from it on the south bank, the Festival Hall and neighbouring concert halls. For the rest it was the depressing view of old wharves, cranes and warehouses. But now with these eyesores even less pleasing to look upon through neglect as they go out of business, the Greater London Council has what Londoners feel are exciting plans to buy up these properties for redevelopment and so alter the face of riverside London that by the 1980s Parisians will change from being derisory to being envious.

To say that Rennie's bridge has been transported stone-by-stone to its new setting is hardly accurate. Rennie's structure weighed 130,000 tons. The tonnage of stone shiped to America was 10,000.

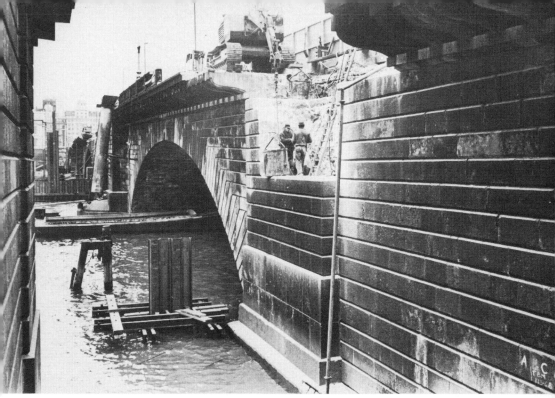

Removing stones from the Bridge in London

Arrival of stones in Arizona

Above: City builder Robert P. McCullogh, left, and C. V. Wood, master planner

British engineer Robert Beresford supervising reassembly of London Bridge

*Stages in reconstruction
of London Bridge*

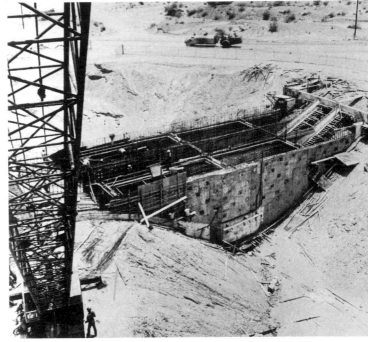

Artist's sketch of London Bridge in its new setting

What accounts for the discrepancy is that the bridge at Lake Havasu City merely has the appearance of being London Bridge.

What has been built at Lake Havasu City is a five-arch concrete bridge with facings of stone from London Bridge. The balustrades are there all right, not Rennie's original parapets but the stonework which was added at each edge of the carriageway of the bridge when it was widened in 1902, and there are other slabs of stone weighing from half a ton to five tons to be seen here and there. But the broad profile of the bridge, although it looks like the original, is in fact a concrete structure with granite facings stuck on like tiles on a bathroom wall. For example, the stones with which the arches of Rennie's bridge were constructed were massive pieces of granite up to six feet in length, more than a foot in depth and a couple of feet wide. From these, parings were taken of four inches in width to form the 'tiles' to stick on to the concrete structure at Lake Havasu.

Nevertheless, the shipping of ten thousand tons of stone in blocks of two to five tons across the Atlantic was no mean feat. The operation was started in the spring of 1968. Pieces that could be used as they existed—balustrades and the like—were taken downstream to the Surrey Commercial Docks and shipped from there. The other pieces that required cutting into slivers for the facing of the concrete bridge at Lake Havasu were taken to the Merivale Quarries in Devon and when the work was done on them they were shipped out of Dartmouth. Taken from England, through the Panama Canal to the west coast of the States, the stone was unloaded in Los Angeles harbour, from where it went by truck the three hundred miles inland to Lake Havasu.

Each piece of stone had a coded number painted on it (by teenage apprentice Alan Saines) designating its exact position in the bridge, with Us, for upstream, and Ds (downstream) indicating which side of the structure identical pieces were taken from. Then like a jigsaw puzzle all was to be reassembled at the new site —described by McCulloch's as something which 'should rank in history as one of man's most unique construction feats'.

In the first year, when some three thousand tons found their way across the Atlantic, the stones were loaded loose in two chartered ships. Not unnaturally by shipping them this way more than a few of the pieces suffered damage in transit. Also when unloaded there was such a mish-mash of stones for the people at the other end to delve through to find the pieces they wanted that it was decided that this method was so inefficient as to be downright un-American. It was then, with something like a third of the job done, McCulloch's came to the conclusion that they should call in the Johnson Line, a Swedish firm which runs a thriving container-ship route from Europe to America's western seaboard. The stone was containerized and at once the whole thing became a much more efficient operation.

To make for speedier loading and unloading of the stone it was packed in open-top containers, exposure to the elements not being likely to do it any harm after more than a century of being exposed to the London climate. At the American end the engineers received in advance the detailed list of precisely which pieces made up each fifteen-ton load of stone per container, and in that way they stored the containers and drew from the material in sequence as the rebuilding progressed.

Rennie's 1,005 feet bridge had no hope of spanning the Colorado River, let alone the waters of Lake Havasu, so the purchasers evolved an ingenious plan to provide it with something to span. The city-to-be is growing up at a location on the lakefront where there is a peninsula which juts out into the lake and on which stretched the old military airfield, now converted into Lake Havasu City's commercial airport. The narrow neck of this peninsula, at the shoreline, is a mile wide and McCulloch's decided to make this into a scenic waterway, which would turn the peninsula into an island and provide a water hazard for London Bridge to overcome. An advantage of this scheme was that the bridge could be constructed on dry land, without the necessity of coffer dams and all the other complications of getting firm foundations established in a river or other waterway. Having completed the bridge the canal could be cut to let the water flow under it.

The customs and excise department of the United States Government co-operated in the whole venture by reaching a friendly decision as to how much import duty would have to be paid on bringing Rennie's bridge into their country. They classified it as 'a large antique'—free of duty.

The Corporation of the City of London co-operated with the desire of McCulloch's to bring to their ceremony of laying the foundation stone of the bridge in its new setting something of the dignity of the original ceremony on the Thames on 15th June 1825.

The Lord Mayor of London was flown to Lake Havasu and on 23rd September 1968 he went through the procedure of putting in place the first stone. An incongruous but impressive figure in the full trappings of his office, nothing quite like it had ever before been seen under the hot desert sun of Arizona. For those lucky enough to be invited the richly embossed admission cards were an exact replica, undated, of those for the original ceremony on the Thames in 1825.

The actual opening of the bridge on 10th October 1971 brought the climax of the symbolic linking of old and new. An estimated 50,000, some in Old English costume, poured in from all over the west, and the inevitable traffic jams were sorted out by sheriffs in stetsons, carrying pistols on their hips. Sir Peter Studd, Lord Mayor of London, dressed in his traditional robes, was joined by Governor Jack Williams of Arizona in pulling the cord to open the bridge. As they did so a huge hot-air balloon in the colours of the Union Jack, rose into the air followed by three thousand pigeons. Indians in all kinds of tribal headdress and costumes took part in the ceremony and at the banquet held that night on the bridge the menu of lobster and roast beef was that placed before William IV at the other opening of the bridge in 1831.

In view of the fact that the London Bridge at Lake Havasu is merely clad in the garb of the original, the purist might be prompted to denounce it as phoney. But there is nothing unusual about facing on a bridge of a material other than that which holds it up. The modern Waterloo Bridge, for example, is a concrete structure with facing of Portland stone. Numerous other bridges and buildings are similarly cloaked in what is technically called 'ashlar' and nobody objects.

Had they so wished, the McCulloch organization *could* have been more literal about rebuilding London Bridge stone-by-stone at the new site. They could have made it a genuine stone arch bridge as Rennie's was, repeating his whole building procedure with the same complete pieces of stone that he had used. But the time, labour and expense involved would have ruled it out as a viable project. To take just one aspect: merely to transport all the stone required over to America would have cost them more than they paid for the bridge.

But after all, what does it matter? The bridge at Lake Havasu City that was opened on 10th October 1971, *looks* like Rennie's London Bridge. Better for it to survive, even in the form of a mock-up, than to have been broken up and sold off for the value of the granite and thus to disappear altogether as an entity.

It does at least make an impressive memorial to John Rennie, engineer.

Acknowledgements

The author wishes to acknowledge the help derived from the three books *Lives of the Engineers*, by Samuel Smiles, *Autobiography of Sir John Rennie* and *John Rennie*, by Cyril T. G. Boucher, and the personal assistance in gathering his material from Major Rennie Maudslay, P. M. Cadell, of the National Library of Scotland, and the library staff of the Institution of Civil Engineers.

Index

Lune Aqueduct, 8
Lune, river, 28

MACADAM, John, 7, 8, 102–3, 121
Macintosh, Martha (Mrs Rennie), 68
Manchester, 122
Manchester Ship Canal, 62
Marconi, 39
Maudslay, Major Rennie, 65
Maugham, Somerset, 20
Meikle, Andrew, 12–13, 19, 20, 22, 25, 26, 62, 67
McCulloch Organization, 9–11, 145–55
Messina, 95
Montague, William, 134
Morrison, Sir Herbert, 16, 107, 109, 150
Murdock, William, 62
Musselburgh, 15, 90

NAPOLEON, 46, 82, 83
Narrows Bridge, 95
Nash, John, 73, 134
Newcastle, 14, 17, 49
Newhaven Harbour, 8
Newton Stewart Bridge, 8
Nicholas, Grand Duke, 27
Norfolk Broads, 42
Northern Lights, Commissioners of, 40–52, 57

OBSERVER, 105
Old Mortality, 43
Orrery, Earl of, 31
Overs, John, 125–6
Overs, Mary, 125–6

PAISLEY, 60
Paris, 27, 153
Paterson, J. Wilson, 15
Payne, A., 110
Peel, Sir Robert, 32
Pennant, Thomas, 131
Perth High School, 25

Peterhead, 116–19
Phantassie, 12, 14, 15, 18, 22, 23, 25, 26, 68, 73, 109
Plymouth Breakwater, 73, 83
Preston Mill, 19, 30

QUEBEC BRIDGE, 94

RAEBURN, Sir Henry, 65
Ramsgate Harbour, 8, 40, 59
Revesby, 45
Rennie, Agnes, 22
Rennie, Anna, 68
Rennie, George, 22, 24, 26, 67, 68, 69, 70, 71, 77, 78
Rennie, Henrietta, 22, 23
Rennie, James, 22, 23, 68
Rennie, Jane, 68
Rennie, Janet, 22
Rennie, Jean, 22
Rennie, Marion, 22
Rennie, Martha, 68, 75
Rennie, Sir John, 9, 28, 31, 39, 40, 62, 64, 70, 71, 74, 75, 78, 112, 116, 119
Rennie, William, 67
Rennie Street, 79
Rennie's Wharf, 78
Robbins, F. W., 12
Robison, Dr John, 27, 31
Rome, 27
Royal Society, 45

SANDRINGHAM, 42
Scott, Sir Walter, 43
Scottish National Trust, 18
Severn, river, 39
Shelley, 68
Shrapnel, Henry, 38
Smeaton, John, 34, 40
Smiles, Samuel, 13, 15, 23, 25, 33, 58, 62, 92, 102–3
Smirke, Robert, 134
Smith, Thomas, 50
Soane, John, 134
Soham and Bottesham Fens, 43
Soho (Birmingham), 28, 33